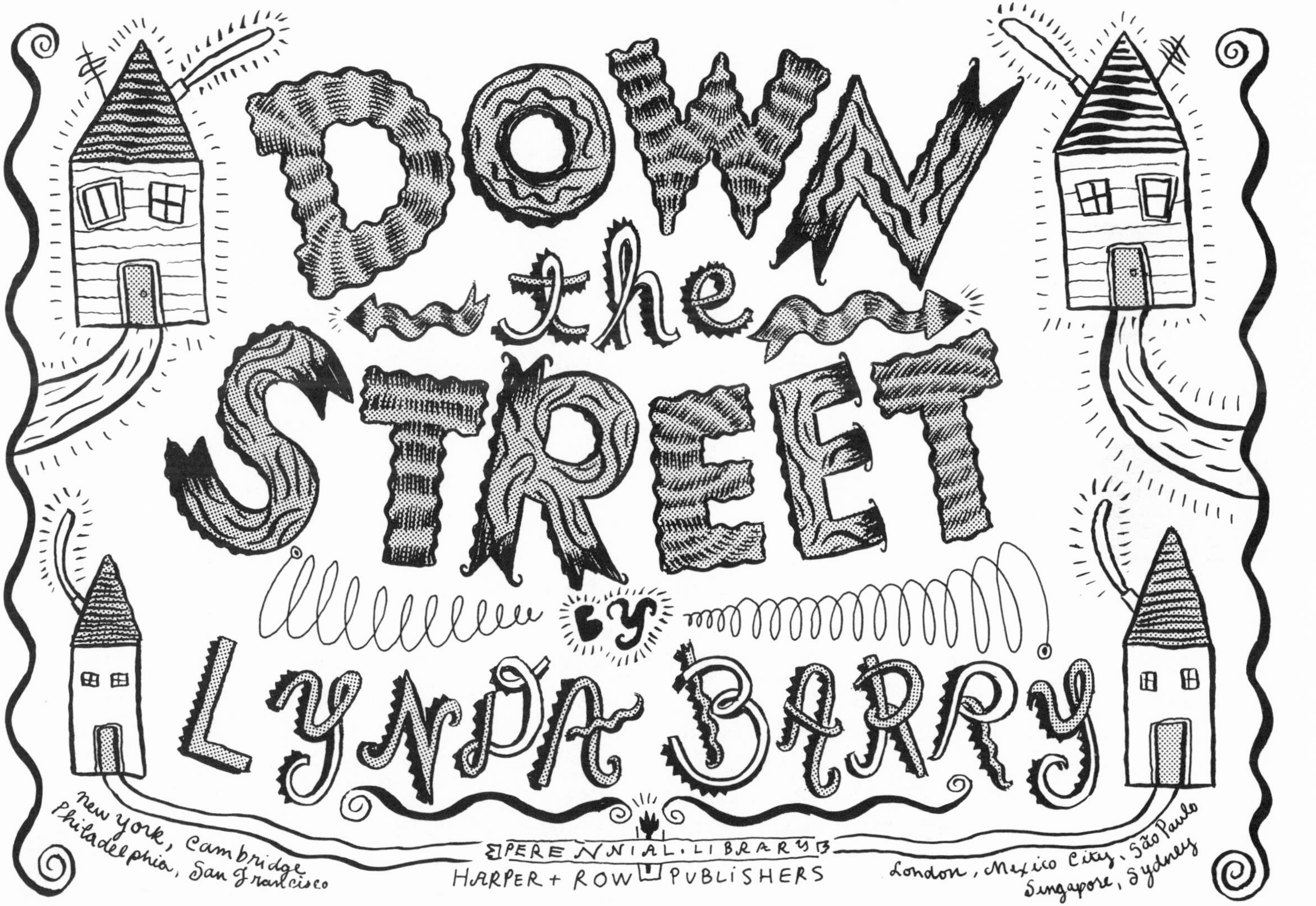
DOWN the STREET
by
LYNDA BARRY
New York, Cambridge
Philadelphia, San Francisco
PERENNIAL LIBRARY
HARPER + ROW PUBLISHERS
London, Mexico City, São Paulo
Singapore, Sydney

 FOR information, address HARPER + ROW, PUBLISHERS, INC., 10 east 53rd street, NEW YORK, NEW YORK 10022. PUBLISHED SIMULTANEOUSLY IN Canada by Fitzhenry + Whiteside Limited, Toronto. FIRST EDITION Library of CONGRESS CATALOG CARD NUMBER: 88-45304 → ISBN: 0-06-096304-2 SPECIAL THANKS TO: LIZ DARHANSOFF THIS IS a BOOK OF PURE FICTION INCLUDING SOME OF THE SPELLING. DESIGN BY LYNDA BARRY + SUPERNATURAL LOVE THANG: RICK KOT .. ALTERNATE: ELISHEVA URBAS
MIXING AND SOUND EFFECTS: IRA GLASS FUNK LORD OF USA: MATT GROENING
PALEOMAGNETIC CONSULTANT: MARGY ROCHLIN SEMAPHORE INSTRUCTOR: NICOLE HOLLANDER
88 89 90 91 92 HOR 10 9 8 7 6 5 4 3 2 1

SCHOOL
HOPSCOTCH
CHALK
ERASER
CHEWED GUM
SCIENCE PROJECTS
MAPS
PENCILS
MILK
SPITWAD
PAPER
LUNCHPAIL
MRS BROGAN
THE CLASS GERBIL
YOUR DESK
ART PROJECTS
MEAT BLANKET
The ENCYCLOPEDIA
THE PENCIL SHARPENER IS NOT A TOY!
Aa Bb Cc Dd Ee Ff Gg Hh Ii Jj Kk Ll Mm Nn Oo Pp Qq Rr Ss Tt Uu Vv Ww Xx Yy Zz

the NEW YEAR
BY LYNDA BARRY © 1987
THIS YEAR IT TURNS OUT ME AND MY COUSIN MARLYS ARE GOING TO BE IN THE SAME ROOM, ROOM 9, MISS MARTLES'S CLASS. WE ARE DOOMED.
YOU HAVE YOUR MILK MONEY?
ARNA Room 9
YEAH.
THANKS, MOM.
WE HAVE HEARD STORIES ABOUT MISS MARTLES FROM WHEN MARLYS'S SISTER MAYBONNE HAD HER IN THE SIXTH GRADE. WE HEARD THAT SHE THROWS HER CHALK WHEN SHE'S MAD AND PLAYS "WHEN JOHNNY COMES MARCHING HOME AGAIN" ON THE ACCORDIAN. AND THAT SHE MAKES YOU STICK YOUR FIST IN THE AIR DURING THE "HURRAH HURRAH" PART AND YELLS "FEELING! MORE FEELING!"
YOU'RE SURE YOU HAVE YOUR MILK MONEY?
YES.
YOU'RE SURE.
YES!
LET ME SEE IT.
MOM.
ARNA Room 9

WE'VE HEARD SHE MAKES YOU DO ABOUT A THOUSAND SQUAT JUMPS FOR P.E. AND ALSO THOSE MODERN DANCE EXERCISES THAT SHE GETS FROM A BOOK, WHERE YOU HAVE TO RUN ACROSS THE PLAYFIELD RIGHT BY THE LIBRARY WINDOWS AND PRETEND YOU'RE AN ANGRY TREE.
WHAT IF SHE MAKES US SIT IN ORDER OF HOW SMART WE ARE? THAT MEANS I'LL BE RIGHT UP FRONT BY HER DESK.
THAT'S NOT EVEN FAIR!
JUST 'CAUSE I'M A GIFTED CHILD!

MAYBONNE SAID THE ONLY GOOD PART ABOUT MISS MARTLES WAS HER PET BIRD DONALD WHO COULD HOLD A PENCIL IN HIS MOUTH. BUT THEN SOMEONE GAVE DONALD A MILKDUD. MAYBONNE WARNED US: DON'T YOU NEVER BRING NO MILK DUDS IN YOUR LUNCH. THIS IS GOING TO BE THE WORST YEAR OF OUR LIVES.
QUIT THINKIN' YOU'RE SO COOL JUST 'CAUSE YOU'RE A PATROL, ARNOLD.
I WAS ON PATROL LAST YEAR.
I WAS A LIEUTENANT.
READY?
WA-ALK.
STOP

THE FIRST DAY
BY LYNDA BARRY ©1987
THE BELL RANG AND WE WENT TO OUR NEW ROOM AND LINED UP IN TWO LINES OUTSIDE THE DOOR AND THOMAS OTIS KEPT SHOVING KENNY BOTTS OVER INTO THE GIRLS' LINE LIKE HE'S ALWAYS BEEN DOING AND PROBABLY ALWAYS WILL DO, FOREVER AND EVER, WORLD WITHOUT END.

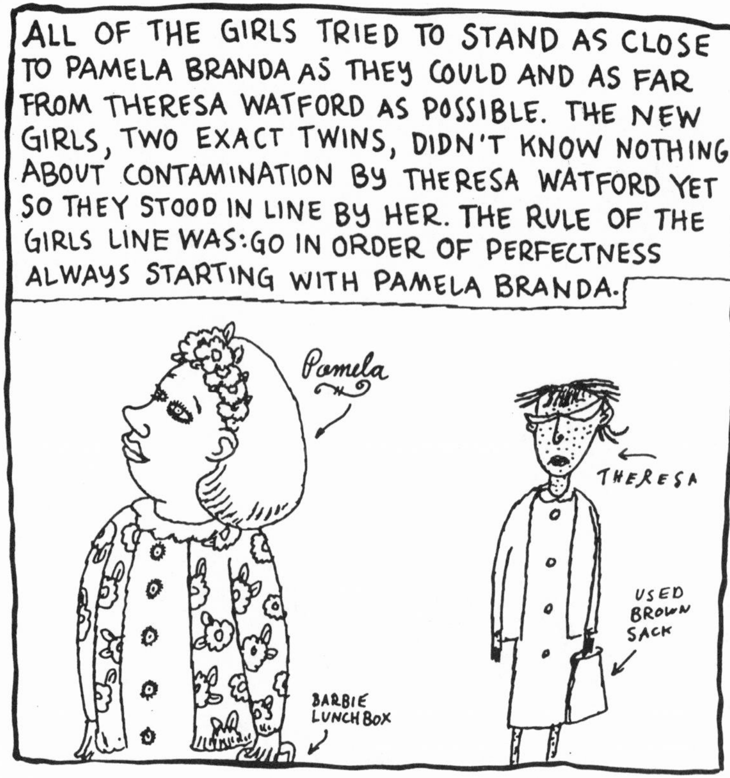
ALL OF THE GIRLS TRIED TO STAND AS CLOSE TO PAMELA BRANDA AS THEY COULD AND AS FAR FROM THERESA WATFORD AS POSSIBLE. THE NEW GIRLS, TWO EXACT TWINS, DIDN'T KNOW NOTHING ABOUT CONTAMINATION BY THERESA WATFORD YET SO THEY STOOD IN LINE BY HER. THE RULE OF THE GIRLS LINE WAS: GO IN ORDER OF PERFECTNESS ALWAYS STARTING WITH PAMELA BRANDA.
Pamela
THERESA
USED BROWN SACK
BARBIE LUNCH BOX

IN THE BOYS' LINE THERE WAS TONY AND VINCENT THE TWO BEST FRIENDS, THE ONES EVERY GIRL WAS SECRETLY IN LOVE WITH INCLUDING PAMELA. INCLUDING THERESA. INCLUDING ME, MY COUSIN MARLYS AND EVERY GIRL IN THE WORLD. IF WE GET SEATED BY THE ALPHABET, I'LL BE RIGHT BEHIND VINCENT AND I'LL GET TO STARE AT THE BACK OF HIS HEAD ALL I WANT. PLEASE, JESUS.

AND TODAY THERE'S THIS CERTAIN SMELL, THE TRUE SMELL OF SCHOOL THAT YOU CAN ONLY SMELL ON THE FIRST DAY WHEN YOU'RE STANDING IN THE HALL WEARING NEW CLOTHES WAITING FOR THE NEW TEACHER TO COME AROUND THE CORNER AND OPEN THE DOOR. WE HEAR SOME KEYS AND THERE SHE IS, MISS MARTLES. AND EVERYONE STOPS TALKING AND TRIES TO FIGURE OUT DO WE HATE HER OR DO WE LIKE HER?

MISS MARTLES
BY LYNDA BARRY © 1987
WELL IF YOU WANT TO KNOW ABOUT OUR NEW TEACHER, HER NAME IS MISS MARTLES. SHE GOTS WHAT YOU CALL THEM SHRIMPY EYES. THE KIND WHERE IF YOU TURN A TELESCOPE BACKWARDS AND LOOK AT YOUR FRIEND AND ALL YOU SEE IS THIS MIDGET EYEBALL STARING AT YOU? IT'S BECAUSE OF HER GLASSES. IN REALITY SHE GOTS THE REGULAR KINDS OF EYES BEHIND THERE, YOU KNOW.

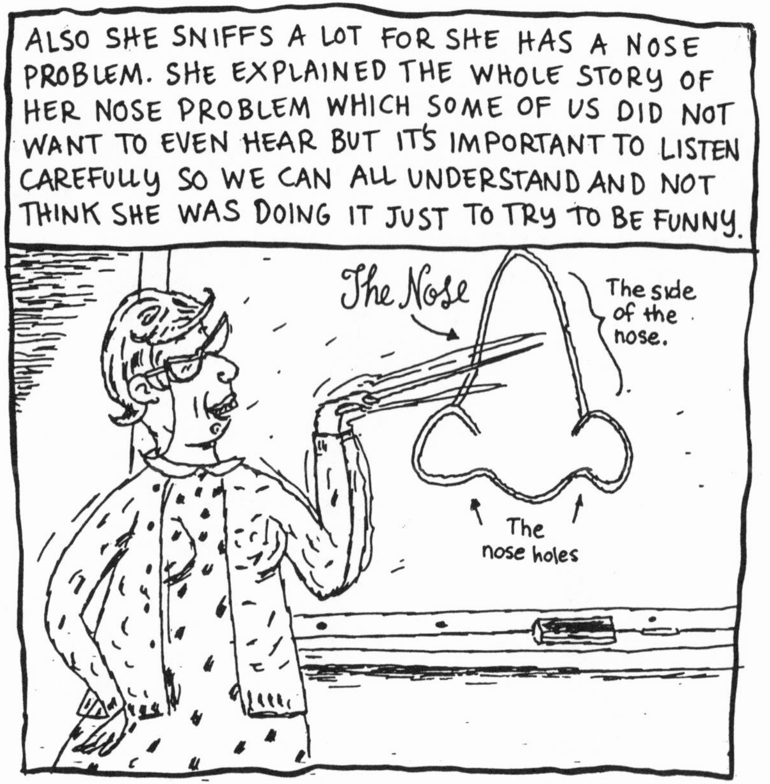
ALSO SHE SNIFFS A LOT FOR SHE HAS A NOSE PROBLEM. SHE EXPLAINED THE WHOLE STORY OF HER NOSE PROBLEM WHICH SOME OF US DID NOT WANT TO EVEN HEAR BUT IT'S IMPORTANT TO LISTEN CAREFULLY SO WE CAN ALL UNDERSTAND AND NOT THINK SHE WAS DOING IT JUST TO TRY TO BE FUNNY.
The Nose
The side of the nose.
The nose holes

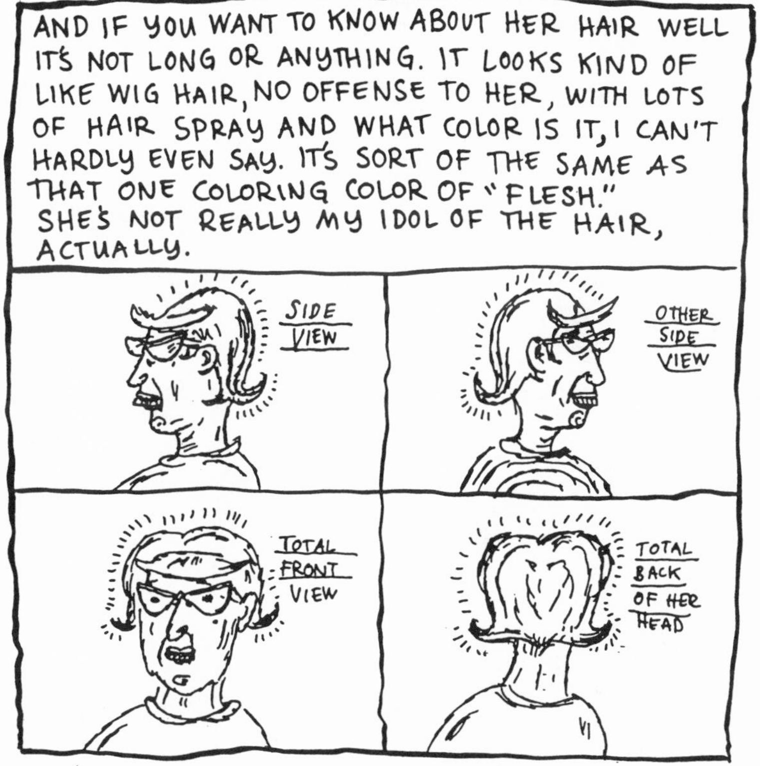
AND IF YOU WANT TO KNOW ABOUT HER HAIR WELL IT'S NOT LONG OR ANYTHING. IT LOOKS KIND OF LIKE WIG HAIR, NO OFFENSE TO HER, WITH LOTS OF HAIR SPRAY AND WHAT COLOR IS IT, I CAN'T HARDLY EVEN SAY. IT'S SORT OF THE SAME AS THAT ONE COLORING COLOR OF "FLESH." SHE'S NOT REALLY MY IDOL OF THE HAIR, ACTUALLY.
SIDE VIEW
OTHER SIDE VIEW
TOTAL FRONT VIEW
TOTAL BACK OF HER HEAD

ANYWAY ALL THAT HAPPENED WAS ME AND MY COUSIN ARNA WERE IN THE LUNCH LINE AND TWO GIRLS FROM MISS THOMPSON'S, THE BEAUTIFUL TEACHER WHO WEARS WHITE BOOTS AND A FALL, STOOD OVER BY US AND STARTED ACTING SO BIG, SAYING WHAT IF THEY HAD GOT MISS MARTLES INSTEAD, BARF, SHE WAS SO DEFECTIVE, ALL THAT. WE IGNORED THEM UNTIL THEY PINCHED THEIR EYES UP GOING SNIFF SNIFF SNIFF, "OH WHO AM I? WHO AM I?" SO ME AND ARNA JUST SHOVED THEM DOWN AND THAT'S WHY WE GOT SENT TO THE OFFICE, OK?

SPELLING
LYNDA BARRY ©1987
SOME PEOPLE ARE JUST NATURALLY GOOD SPELLERS BUT IT DOES NOT MEAN THEIR LIFE IS PERFECT BECAUSE OF IT. MY COUSIN MARLYS FOR EXAMPLE CAN SPELL ANYTHING: SPATULA, DISQUALIFY, CHIHUAHUA, MEDITERRENEAN.
BORIS. B-O-R-I-S. NATASHIA. N-A-T-A-S
SHUT UP FOR AT LEAST ONE SECOND O.K. MARLYS I'M TRYING TO HEAR.
BOREES.
WE MUST GET SQUIRREL.
SQUIRREL. S-Q-U-I-R-R-E-L.
EVERY YEAR WHEN THEY HAND OUT THE SPELLING FOR WORD MASTERY BOOKS, MARLYS ALWAYS RAISES HER HAND TO TELL THE TEACHER GUESS WHAT, SHE KNOWS ALL THE WORDS ALREADY. YOU'D THINK THIS MIGHT MAKE A GOOD IMPRESSION BUT IT DOESN'T.
AND YOU ALREADY KNOW I'M A GIFTED CHILD, RIGHT MISS MARTLES?
SPELLING FOR WORD MASTERY

AND FOR AS GOOD OF A SPELLER AS MARLYS IS SHE CAN NEVER BE IN THE ALL CITY SPELLING BEE AGAIN FOR HURLING ERASERS WHEN SHE MISSED ON "PHOSPHORUS" AND FOR KICKING AT THE TEACHER WHO CAME TO GET HER WHEN MARLYS WOULD NOT GO SIT DOWN.
DO OVERS! DO OVERS! DO OVERS! DO OVERS! DO OVERS! DO OVERS!
COME NOW MARLYS. LET'S BE GOOD CITIZENS, SHALL WE?

OF COURSE THIS INCIDENT WENT ON HER PERMANENT RECORD WHICH WILL FOLLOW HER FOR THE REST OF HER LIFE.
FRANKLY, WE'D HIRE YOU IN A SECOND IF IT WEREN'T FOR THIS NASTY BIT OF BUSINESS ABOUT YOUR BEHAVIOR AT A CERTAIN SPELLING BEE.
I'M VERY SORRY, MISS.

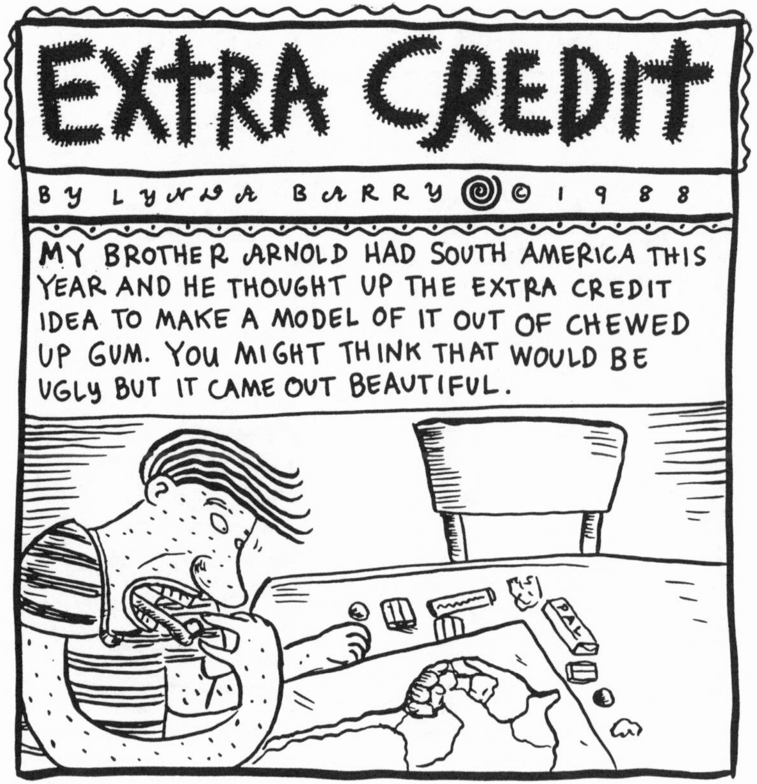

EXTRA CREDIT
BY LYNDA BARRY © 1988
MY BROTHER ARNOLD HAD SOUTH AMERICA THIS YEAR AND HE THOUGHT UP THE EXTRA CREDIT IDEA TO MAKE A MODEL OF IT OUT OF CHEWED UP GUM. YOU MIGHT THINK THAT WOULD BE UGLY BUT IT CAME OUT BEAUTIFUL.
PAL

HE SAID GUM WAS PERFECT BECAUSE THERE'S 13 KINDS FOR THE 13 COUNTRIES AND GUM LASTS GOOD. WE HAVE SOME STUCK ON THE SIDE OF THE GARAGE FROM WAY LAST SUMMER AND IT'S STILL THERE. HE SPENT $2.49 ON GUM FOR THAT MODEL. WE ALL THOUGHT HE WAS GOING TO GET AN "A" FOR SURE.
PAT PAT PAT

HE SAID THE HARD PART WAS DRAWING THE COUNTRIES RIGHT ON THE CARDBOARD. AFTER THAT ALL HE HAD TO DO WAS REMEMBER WHICH GUM WAS WHICH COUNTRY. Uruguay Was CINCHY: TWO DENTYNES. BUT BRAZIL TOOK SO MUCH BAZOOKA, ARNOLD SAYS EVEN JUST THE SMELL OF THAT GUM STILL MAKES HIM ABOUT THROW UP.

WHEN HE PRESENTED IT TO MRS. BROGAN SHE TOLD HIM IT COULD SPREAD DISEASE. I HAD MRS. BROGAN LAST YEAR AND SHOULD HAVE KNOWN TO TELL HIM THE TOPIC OF HER WHOLE LIFE IS GERMS. ARNOLD SAID JUST SPRAY IT WITH LYSOL, KILLS GERMS ON CONTACT, DON'T THROW IT OUT! BUT NO.
THAT'S WHY YOU SHOULD NEVER MENTION SOUTH AMERICA TO MY BROTHER.
CLASS, WHAT VALUABLE LESSON HAS ARNOLD HELPED US LEARN TODAY?

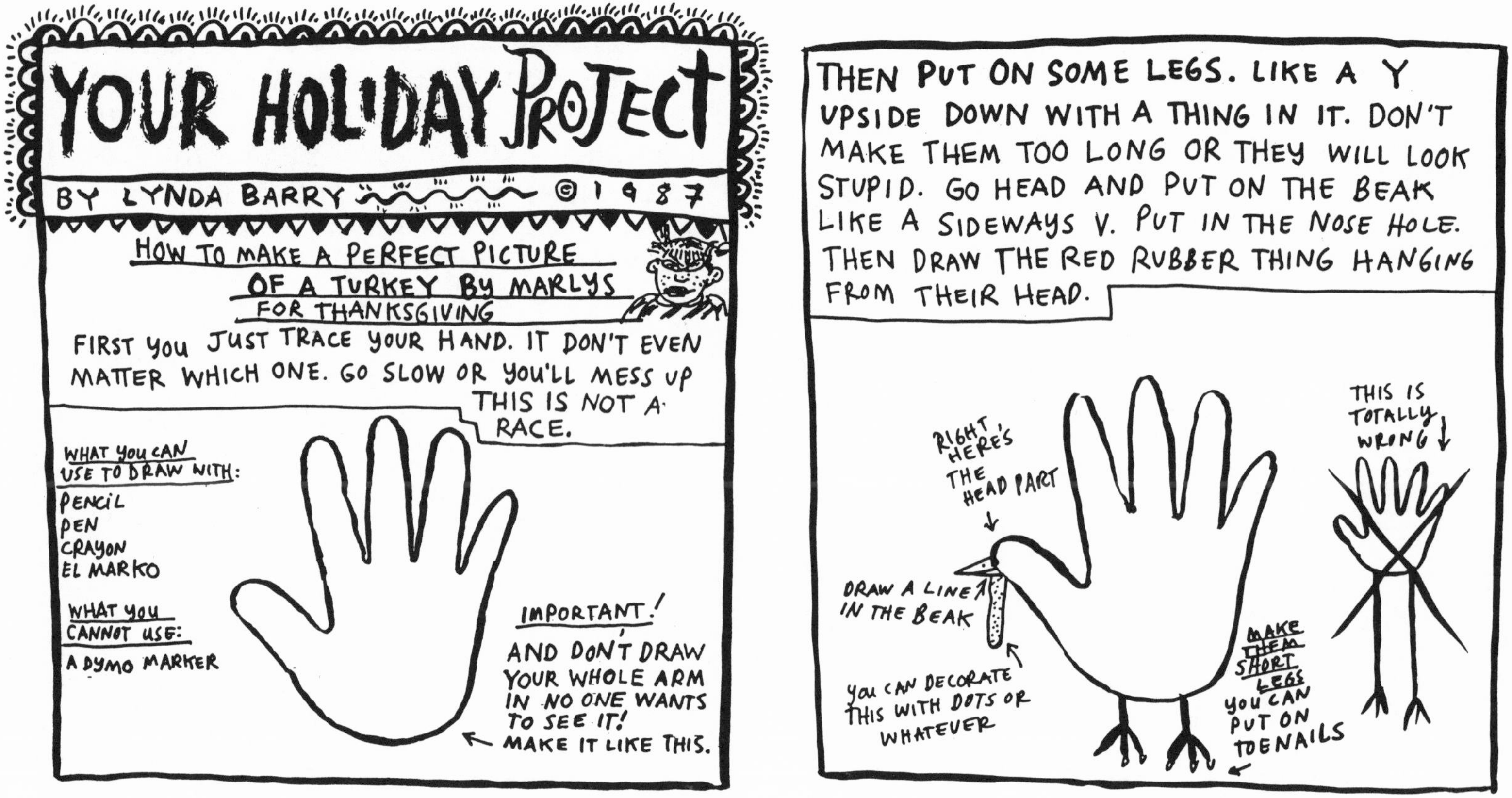

YOUR HOLIDAY PROJECT
BY LYNDA BARRY ©1987
HOW TO MAKE A PERFECT PICTURE OF A TURKEY BY MARLYS FOR THANKSGIVING
FIRST YOU JUST TRACE YOUR HAND. IT DON'T EVEN MATTER WHICH ONE. GO SLOW OR YOU'LL MESS UP
THIS IS NOT A RACE.
WHAT YOU CAN USE TO DRAW WITH:
PENCIL
PEN
CRAYON
EL MARKO
WHAT YOU CANNOT USE:
A DYMO MARKER
IMPORTANT!
AND DON'T DRAW YOUR WHOLE ARM IN NO ONE WANTS TO SEE IT!
MAKE IT LIKE THIS.
THEN PUT ON SOME LEGS. LIKE A Y UPSIDE DOWN WITH A THING IN IT. DON'T MAKE THEM TOO LONG OR THEY WILL LOOK STUPID. GO HEAD AND PUT ON THE BEAK LIKE A SIDEWAYS V. PUT IN THE NOSE HOLE. THEN DRAW THE RED RUBBER THING HANGING FROM THEIR HEAD.
RIGHT HERE'S THE HEAD PART
DRAW A LINE IN THE BEAK
YOU CAN DECORATE THIS WITH DOTS OR WHATEVER
MAKE THEM SHORT LEGS
YOU CAN PUT ON TOENAILS
THIS IS TOTALLY WRONG

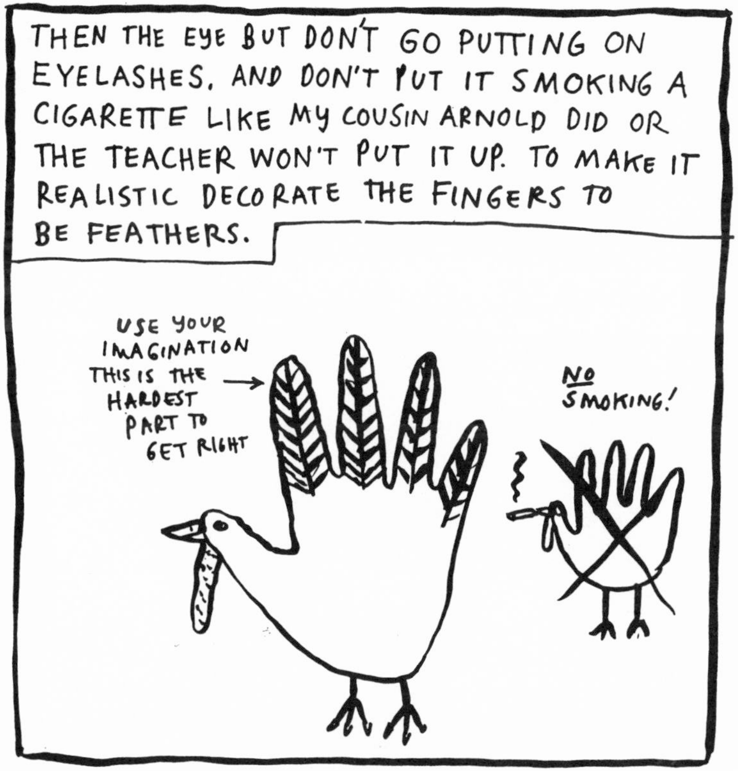
THEN THE EYE BUT DON'T GO PUTTING ON EYELASHES. AND DON'T PUT IT SMOKING A CIGARETTE LIKE MY COUSIN ARNOLD DID OR THE TEACHER WON'T PUT IT UP. TO MAKE IT REALISTIC DECORATE THE FINGERS TO BE FEATHERS.
USE YOUR IMAGINATION THIS IS THE HARDEST PART TO GET RIGHT
NO SMOKING!

FOR EXTRA CREDIT YOU CAN PUT A WING IN IF YOU ARE GOOD AT ART. IF YOU ARE TALENTED. IF YOU ARE NOT YOU PROBABLY ARE GOING TO WRECK IT UP.
PERSONALLY I LIKE TO PUT A LITTLE HAT THAT'S WHY I GET AN A+ BUT IF YOU DO IT THATS COPYING.
THIS IS A PERFECT DECORATION
WHERE YOU CAN PUT THIS UP:
AT SCHOOL
THE LUNCHROOM
THE OFFICE
THE HALLS
ON THE DOOR
OVER THE CHALKBOARD
AT HOME
THE KITCHEN
THE FRONTROOM
THE BEDROOM
THE FRONT DOOR

LUNCH
BY LYNDA HIP HUGGER BARRY © 1987
ONE THING ABOUT OUR AUNT. SHE MADE THE WORST SANDWICHES IN THE UNIVERSE. HER IDEA OF A SANDWICH WAS A PIECE OF BALOGNA ON A PIECE OF BREAD, THEN A HUNK OF COLD MARGERINE IN THE MIDDLE, THEN SMASH THE OTHER PIECE OF BREAD ON TOP. WHEN YOU BITE A WAD OF COLD MARGERINE YOU CANNOT FORGET IT FOR ABOUT TWO HOURS.
DAMN IT! NOW WHERE'S THEM SANDWICH BAGS?!
ONE FOR MARLYS
ONE FOR FREDDY
BALOGNA
CROCK O' MARGE

MARLYS AND FREDDY HAD TO LUG THESE TERRIBLE SANDWICHES OUT OF PAPER BAGS IN THE LUNCHROOM AND BE SITTING BY THIS ONE GIRL, DELORES, WHO HAD THE GORGEOUS BLACK VINYL BARBIE LUNCHBOX AND INSIDE WERE THE MOST PERFECT SANDWICHES YOU EVER SAW, POTATO CHIPS IN SARAN WRAP, BOTH TWINKIES, A THERMOS FULL OF CHOCOLATE MILK, A NAPKIN WITH ANIMALS ON IT AND A CHOCKS VITAMIN IN A TINY BOX. WELL IT WOULD KILL YOU TO SEE IT ALL, ESPECIALLY IF YOU WERE MARLYS.
FLOWERED HEAD BAND
TRADE YA.
Barbie
MILK

ME AND MY BROTHER GOT THE HOT LUNCHES AND MARLYS AND FREDDY WOULD COME AROUND TRYING TO TRADE THOSE LUMPY SANDWICHES FOR SOME OF OUR MEAT BLANKET. WE ALWAYS SHARED BECAUSE THEY'RE OUR COUSINS, BUT WE NEVER TRADED. YOU COULDN'T EVEN FAKE EAT A SANDWICH LIKE THAT.
THAT DELORES THINKS SHE'S SO BIG JUST 'CAUSE HER LUNCHPAIL LOOKS LIKE A PURSE FROM FRANCE.
SHE WOULDN'T EVEN TRADE ME FOR ONE POTATO CHIP.
FORGET HER.
CHEAP.
MILK
MILK

LATER, MARLYS ALWAYS SAID THAT IT WAS PARTLY BECAUSE OF THOSE SANDWICHES THAT HER WHOLE LIFE WAS WRECKED UNTIL JR. HIGH SCHOOL AND YOU KNOW, I HAVE TO AGREE WITH HER.
HOLY BALLS! THEY FORGOT THEIR DAMN LUNCHES AGAIN.
Marlys M. Room 6
Freddy M. Room 2

BOOK REPORT
BY LYNDA BARRY © 1987
Book Title: What is a Rodent?
Author: Alita Wescott and Carlotta Scott
Copyright: 1962 Pages: 48
by Freddie Room 2
The book tells What is a rodent? They are mammels. There are a lot of kinds. They all want to chew up things.
THE TAILS NOT REALLY A PING PONG PADDLE ITS MADE OF FLESH.
A BEAVER A HARD WORKER
A RAT A FAST RUNNER
A SQUIRREL A GOOD CLIMBER
A PORCUPINE A GOOD STABBER

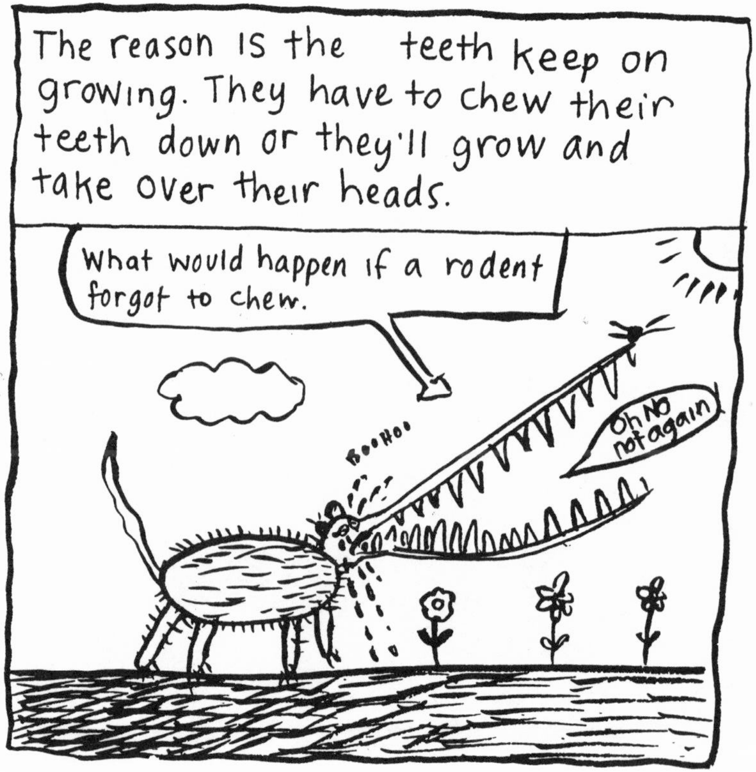
The reason is the teeth keep on growing. They have to chew their teeth down or they'll grow and take over their heads.
What would happen if a rodent forgot to chew.
BOOHOO
Oh No not again

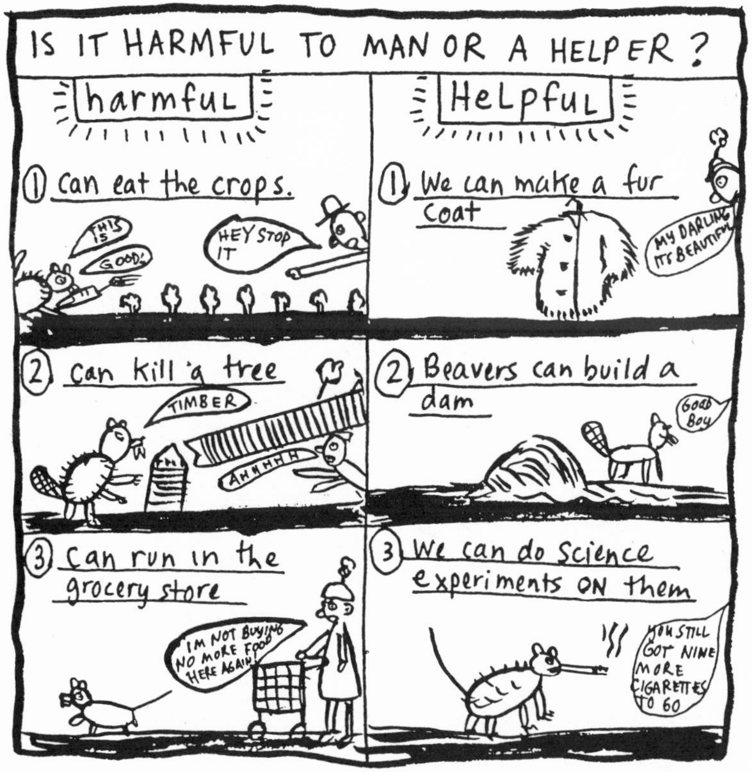

IS IT HARMFUL TO MAN OR A HELPER?
harmful
Helpful
① Can eat the crops.
THIS IS GOOD!
HEY STOP IT
① We can make a fur coat
MY DARLING ITS BEAUTIFUL
② Can kill a tree
TIMBER
AHHHHH
② Beavers can build a dam
GOOD BOY
③ Can run in the grocery store
IM NOT BUYING NO MORE FOOD HERE AGAIN!
③ We can do Science experiments ON them
YOU STILL GOT NINE MORE CIGARETTES TO GO

What was the author trying to Say?
That rodents are exciting.
The End
DRAWING FOR EXTRA CREDIT.
This is not a trace

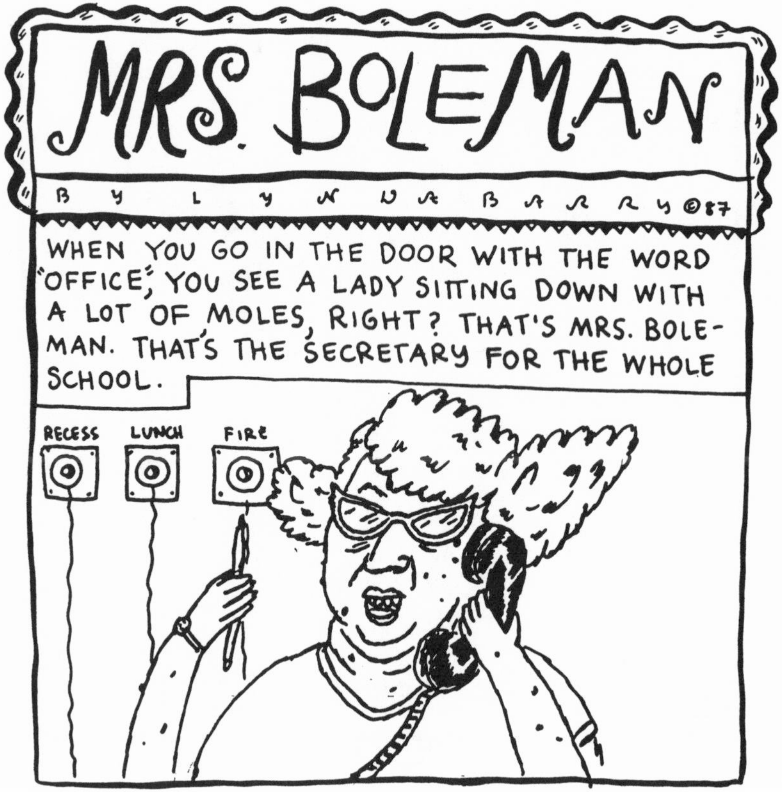
MRS. BOLEMAN
BY LYNDA BARRY ©87
WHEN YOU GO IN THE DOOR WITH THE WORD "OFFICE," YOU SEE A LADY SITTING DOWN WITH A LOT OF MOLES, RIGHT? THAT'S MRS. BOLEMAN. THAT'S THE SECRETARY FOR THE WHOLE SCHOOL.
RECESS
LUNCH
FIRE

WELL I KNOW HER IN REAL LIFE. SHE'S FRIENDS WITH MY MOM AND SHES BEEN OVER AT OUR HOUSE AROUND 900 TIMES. IT WAS MY MOM WHO COMBED OUT HER PERMANENT.
YOW! GOOD GOD! YA TRYIN' TA TEAR MY GOOD DAMN HEAD OFF?
OH HUSH
EASE UP FOR THE LOVE OF CHRIST!
WELL IF YOU'D HOLD YOUR HEAD RIGHT.

THEY KNOW EACH OTHER FROM BOOT CAMP. I'VE ONLY HAD TO LOOK AT THE BORING PICTURE OF THEM ABOUT 8,000 TIMES. IF THEY DRINK WINE, THEN YOU SHOULD HEAR THEM SING. THEY HAVE THIS ONE SONG ABOUT HOW THE CHICKEN IN THE NAVY THEY SAY IS MIGHTY FINE. THEN THE CHICKEN ROLLS OFF THE TABLE AND KILLS ONE OF THEIR FRIENDS. MRS. BOLMAN'S BRAND IS WINSTONS. ALSO SHE WAS BORN WITH A WILD HAIR.
WHAT WAS HER NAME? IDA? IDA STONE. THAT WOMAN THOUGHT SHE WAS QUEEN SHIT OF TURD ISLAND. FROM BOSTON, WASN'T SHE? AND LOOK AT SANDRA. SHE'S BIG AS A HOUSE NOW YOU KNOW.

AND WHAT A SWEARER. ABOUT TEN MILLION SWEARS PER NIGHT. I'LL WHISPER YOU HER FIRST NAME IT'S BEUNICE BOLMAN
DON'T SAY IT SO LOUD!
OFFICE

HOLIDAY BAZAAR
BY LYNDA BARRY ©87
ON THE FREEZING MORNING OF THE SCHOOL'S HOLIDAY BAZAAR, EVERYONE COMES TO THE GYM CARRYING A TRAY OF SOMETHING THEIR MOM MADE WRAPPED IN TIN FOIL, WAX PAPER, OR MAGIC CLING WRAP. WALK CAREFUL BECAUSE IF YOU DROP IT: THE END.
IF I DROP THIS IT'S YOUR FAULT ARNOLD
FLAKE OFF
IT'S YOUR FAULT FOR WALKING IN FRONT OF ME.

THE TEACHER'S HELPERS POINT YOU TO THE RIGHT TABLE DEPENDING ON WHAT YOU BROUGHT. THERE'S A LOT OF COOKIES, ALL KINDS: NORMAL ONES LIKE OATMEAL, GRANDMA ONES LIKE "MOLASSES JINGLES", GORGEOUSLY DECORATED CHRISTMAS ONES YOU FEEL BAD FOR EVEN EATING, AND KINDS YOU NEVER EVEN HEARD OF BEFORE LIKE "YULA MYSTERY BALLS" WHICH LOOK LIKE DIRT CLODS.

THERE'S A LOT OF CUPCAKES, ALL COLORS OF FROSTING. THE BEST ONES HAVE THE LITTLE SILVER METAL BALL DECORATIONS THAT WHEN YOU BITE THEM, YOUR TEETH FEEL LIKE CRACKING. THE SADDEST ARE THE ONES WHERE THE FROSTING GOT YANKED OFF BY THE MAGIC CLING WRAP. THEY BETTER PUT THOSE ON SALE HALF PRICE.
WHAT ARE YOU GOING TO DO WITH THAT FROSTING THAT JUST CAME OFF? I'LL TAKE IT TO THE GARBAGE FOR YOU, OK? OK? HUH?

YOU HAVE TO WAIT UNTIL TONIGHT AFTER THE PAGENT TO BUY ANYTHING SO QUIT WASTING TIME BY PUTTING ON DIBS. TEACHER'S HELPERS DON'T TAKE NO DIBS. AND WHAT'S OUR OPINION OF WHAT'S GOING TO JUST SIT THERE, NO BUYERS? THE PRUNE FILLED YAM SQUARES, ICE BOX BARLEY LOGS, CANDIED HOLIDAY FRUIT LOAF, AND THE YULA DIRT CLODS.
PSSST
HOW MUCH WOULD I HAVE TO PAY YA TO EAT ONE OF THESE?

CHRISTMAS PAGENT
LYNDA BARRY © 1987
"OH HOLY NIGHT THE STARS ARE BRIGHTLY SHINING" MARLYS SINGS OVER AND OVER FOR PRACTICE AS ALL OF US WALK IN THE DARK OVER THE FROZEN MUD IN THE ALLEY ON OUR WAY UP TO THE SCHOOL. ARNOLD JUMPS AND BUSTS ALL THE ICE HE CAN FIND. ITS THE NIGHT OF THE SCHOOL PAGENT.
WHEN WE TURN THE CORNER, WE SEE THE WHOLE SCHOOL JUST COMPLETELY LIT UP. CARS ARE DRIVING UP AND DOWN DROPPING PEOPLE OFF AND THERE'S EVERYBODY EVERYWHERE YELLING "Hi! Hi! Hiya!" ARNOLD SEES HIS FRIEND STEVE AND TAKES OFF RUNNING.

MARLYS AND FREDDY REPORT TO THEIR ROOMS BUT I'M NOT NOTHING IN THE PAGENT THIS YEAR SO I CAN JUST GO WALKING AROUND THE HALLS NOTICING HOW BEING IN YOUR SCHOOL AT NIGHT MAKES EVERYTHING FEEL LIKE IT'S ON ANOTHER PLANET.
RUN'

I CLIMB THE STAIRS TO THE 2ND FLOOR AND LOOK OUT THE WINDOW AND SEE THEM SHUT THE DOORS TO THE GYM. OH NO. IT'S STARTING. I RUN DOWN THE HALL, DOWN THE STEPS, DOWN THE HALL AND SKID IN FRONT OF THE BOYS LAVATORY. NOBODYS AROUND ANYWHERE. I DARE MYSELF TO GO INSIDE. I OPEN THE DOOR AND SEE THEIR STALLS, THEIR SINKS, THEIR MIRROR. THEN WHO KNOWS WHY I SCREAM "MERRY CHRISTMAS FROM ARNA ARNESON!" AND TEAR OUT OF THERE, OUT OF THE SCHOOL AND ACROSS THE BREEZEWAY INTO THE GYM.

WORM REPORT
LYNDA BARRY ©1988
THE SUBJECT OF MY REPORT IS THE GIANT MYSTERY WORM OF AUSTRALIA. A HUGE EARTHWORM TEN FEET LONG THAT LIVED IN THE DIRT. ANOTHER THING IS WHEN IT HEARD YOU WALKING, IT GROANED. THEY CALLED IT THE GROANER.
WORM COMPARED TO PENCIL
A LADY NAMED MILDRED BELLOMY CAUGHT THE WORM BY GRABBING ITS HEAD AND TYING IT IN A KNOT SO IT COULDN'T GO BACK DOWN. YOU MIGHT SAY THAT'S COLD BLOODED OF MILDRED BUT THE GOAL OF HER LIFE WAS THAT WORM. SHE SMOKED CIGARETTES AND WAITED FOR THE WORM TO GIVE UP AND CRAWL OUT. FINALLY HE DID. PEOPLE HAD CALLED HER A LIAR. AT LAST SHE HAD HER PROOF.

HE SMELLED LIKE TAR AND SHE HAD SEEN HIM STICKING HIS HEAD OUT IN HER YARD OFTEN. WHEN SHE PICKED HIM UP HE SHOT OUT POISON ONE FOOT IN ALL DIRECTIONS SO SHE WOULD JUST QUIT HOLDING HIM. HE JUST WANTED TO BE ALONE IN THE DIRT TRAVELING THROUGH ALL HIS MILLIONS OF TUNNELS CAN YOU BLAME HIM?

IN THE BOOK I READ ON IT THERE'S A PICTURE OF MILDRED WITH HER HAND ON TWO FIVE FOOT GLASS TUBES WHERE SHE STORES THE BODY OF THE WORM, ONE HALF IN EACH. AND IF WORMS COME BACK TO LIFE, BOY IS SHE IN FOR IT.

FIRE
BY LYNDA BARRY ©1987
I WAS ASLEEP LIKE NORMAL WHEN MY BROTHER BUSTS INTO MY ROOM YELLING THE SCHOOL'S ON FIRE! THE SCHOOL'S ON FIRE! WE COULD HEAR A MILLION FIRE TRUCKS JUST GOING AND GOING.
RED ALERT! RED ALERT!
THIS IS NOT A DRILL!

FIRST OUR MOM SAID "GET BACK INTO BED," THEN SHE SAID "GET YOUR COATS," THEN SHE SAID "WAIT HERE," THEN SHE SAID "COME WITH ME. BY GOD I BET IT WAS THOSE DAMN WATFORD BOYS. BY GOD I BET IT WAS."
MY CIGARETTES! WHERE'S MY GOD DAMN CIGARETTES!?!
GO LOCK THE DOOR! NO! WHERE ARE MY KEYS!?
JESUS H. CHRIST WHERE ARE MY CIGARETTES?
COME ON YOU TWO HURRY IT UP!
HOLD HANDS DO YOU HEAR ME!?

WE CAN SMELL THE BURNING AND SPARKS ARE FLYING IN OUR BACK YARD AND WE GO RUNNING INTO THE TOTAL PITCH DARK ALLEY, GETTING DRAGGED BY OUR ARMS LIKE OUR NORMAL RUNNING ISN'T GOOD ENOUGH. HAVE YOU EVER RUN IN THE FREEZING NIGHT WEARING JUST YOUR SHOES WITH NO SOCKS? THAT'S THE FEELING OF EMERGENCY.

WE TURN THE CORNER AND IT DOESN'T TAKE A GENIUS TO SEE THAT IT'S THE 6TH GRADER'S PORTABLES THAT ARE ALL ON FIRE. AND EVERYONE IN THE WORLD IS STANDING THERE LIT UP BRIGHT ORANGE IN THEIR PAJAMAS. YOU KNOW HOW IT IS WHEN YOU CAN START TO TELL YOU'RE STARING AT SOMETHING YOU'RE ABOUT TO REMEMBER FOR THE REST OF YOUR WHOLE LIFE?

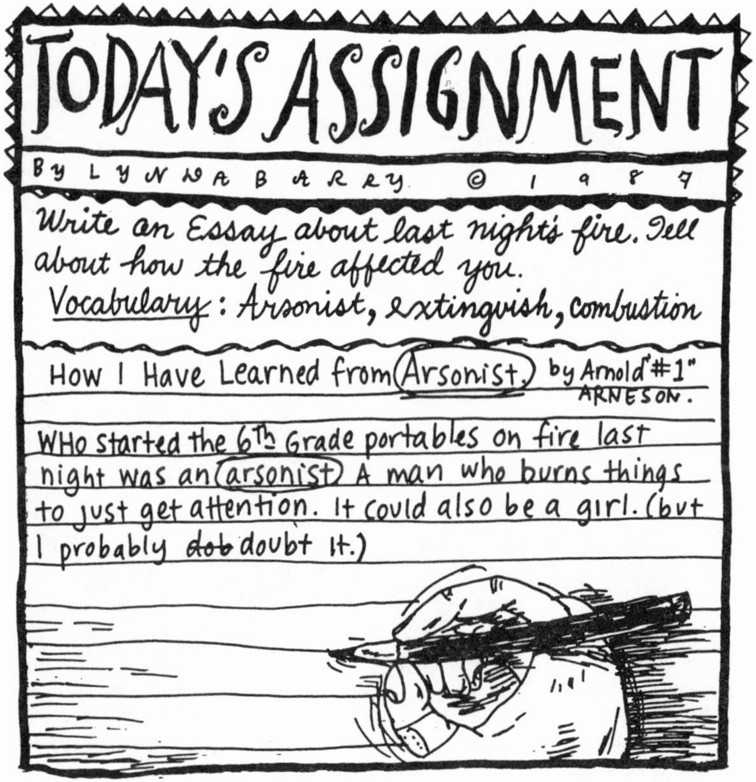

TODAY'S ASSIGNMENT
By Lynda Barry © 1987
Write an Essay about last night's fire. Tell about how the fire affected you.
Vocabulary: Arsonist, extinguish, combustion
How I Have Learned from Arsonist. by Arnold "#1" ARNESON.
WHO started the 6th Grade portables on fire last night was an arsonist A man who burns things to just get attention. It could also be a girl. (but I probably ~~dob~~ doubt it.)

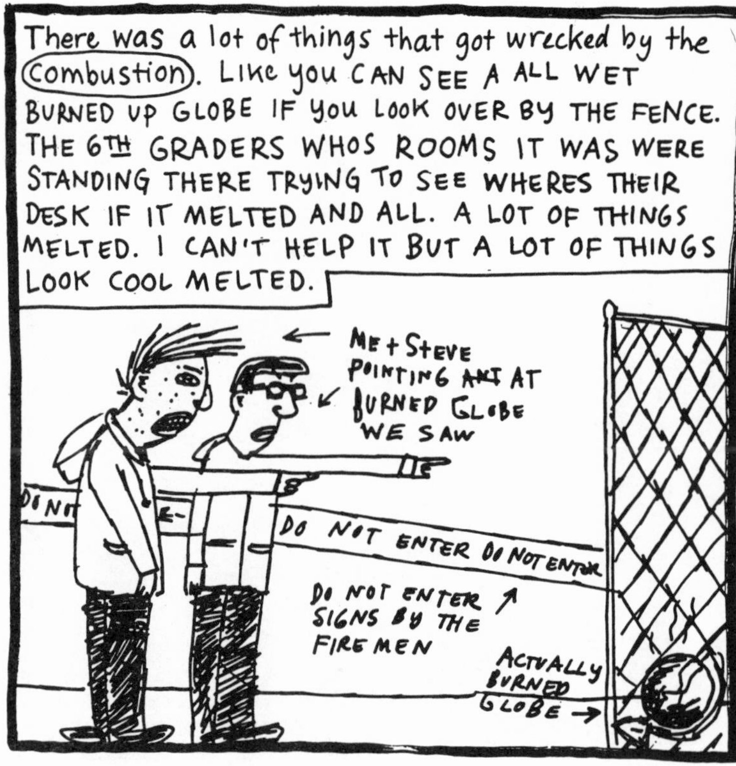

There was a lot of things that got wrecked by the Combustion. Like you CAN SEE A ALL WET BURNED UP GLOBE IF YOU LOOK OVER BY THE FENCE. THE 6TH GRADERS WHOS ROOMS IT WAS WERE STANDING THERE TRYING TO SEE WHERES THEIR DESK IF IT MELTED AND ALL. A LOT OF THINGS MELTED. I CAN'T HELP IT BUT A LOT OF THINGS LOOK COOL MELTED.
ME + STEVE POINTING ~~ANT~~ AT BURNED GLOBE WE SAW
DO NOT ENTER DO NOT ENTER
DO NOT ENTER SIGNS BY THE FIREMEN
ACTUALLY BURNED GLOBE

STARTING PORTABLES ON FIRE IS NOT FUNNY. IF THE ARSONIST WAS TRYING TO BE FUNNY THEN NO ONE IS LAUGHING, MISTER! EXCEPT NORRIS VANCE, WHO GOT IN TROUBLE FOR IT, HE DESERVES IT! WHEN THEY SAW ALL THE ~~CUB~~ CUMBUSTION THE FIREMEN HAD TO EXTINGUISH IT.
HEY MAN WHO STARTED THIS HES GONNA GET IT!
YOU SAID IT LETS GET HIM!
ALL BECAUSE OF HIM, THE FIREMEN HAD TO STAY AROUND UNTIL MORNING.

ALL I HAVE TO SAY ABOUT IT IS IF ME AND MY FRIENDS EVER SEE THAT STUPID IDIOT ARSONIST WE'RE GOING TO LIGHT HIM ON FIRE AND SEE HOW HE LIKES IT. HE'LL HATE IT!! ARNOLD STRIKES AGAIN!
THE END.
by ARNOLD.
ARNOLD IS #1!
HELP!
HELP!
HELP ME
PLEASE HELP ME IF ARNOLD GETS ME I AM DOOMED! HELP SAVE ME
MY HAND
MATCHES. THE EVIDENCE
ARSONIST RUNNING

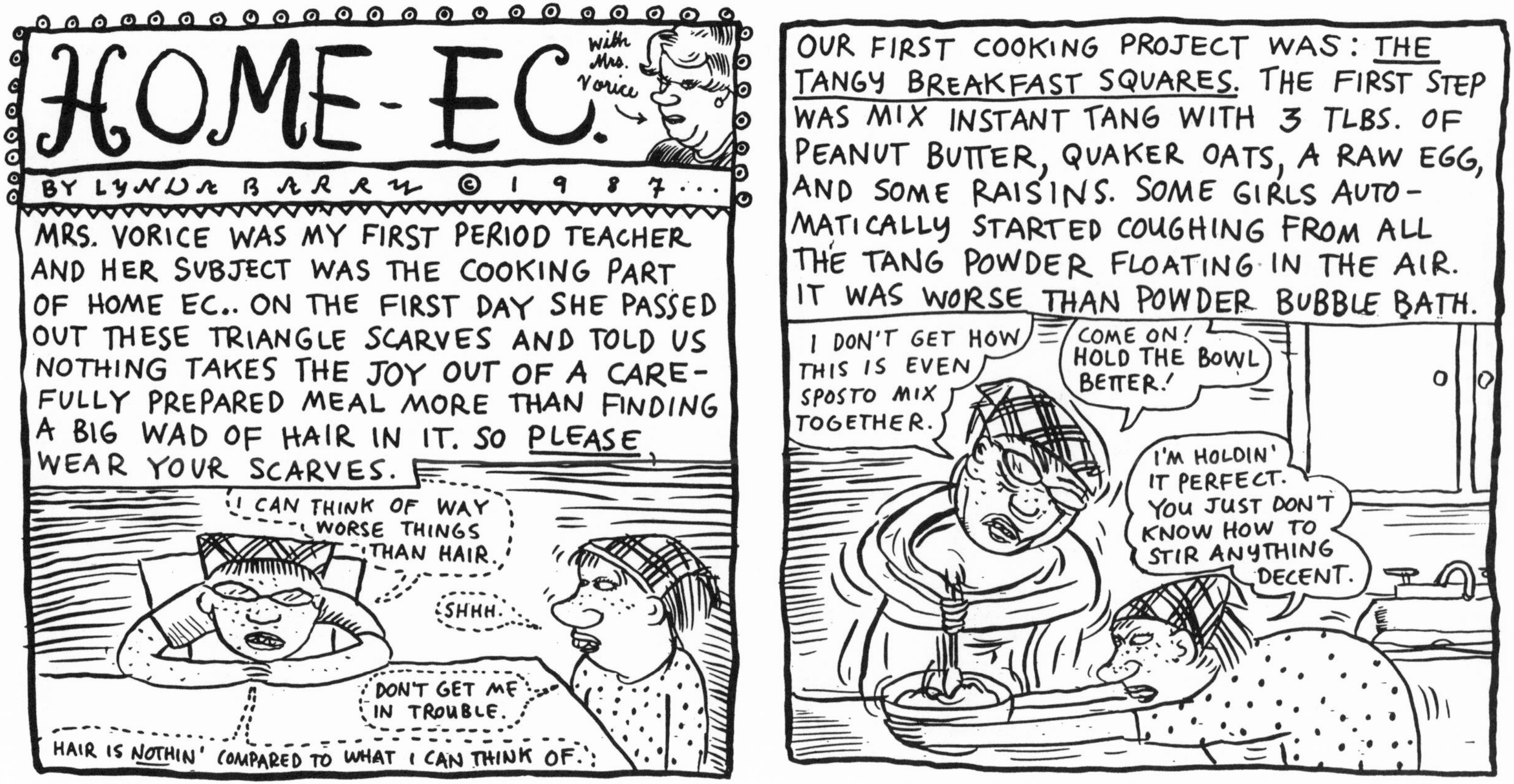
HOME-EC.
with Mrs. Vorice
BY LYNDA BARRY © 1987...
MRS. VORICE WAS MY FIRST PERIOD TEACHER AND HER SUBJECT WAS THE COOKING PART OF HOME EC.. ON THE FIRST DAY SHE PASSED OUT THESE TRIANGLE SCARVES AND TOLD US NOTHING TAKES THE JOY OUT OF A CAREFULLY PREPARED MEAL MORE THAN FINDING A BIG WAD OF HAIR IN IT. SO PLEASE WEAR YOUR SCARVES.
I CAN THINK OF WAY WORSE THINGS THAN HAIR.
SHHH.
DON'T GET ME IN TROUBLE.
HAIR IS NOTHIN' COMPARED TO WHAT I CAN THINK OF.
OUR FIRST COOKING PROJECT WAS: THE TANGY BREAKFAST SQUARES. THE FIRST STEP WAS MIX INSTANT TANG WITH 3 TLBS. OF PEANUT BUTTER, QUAKER OATS, A RAW EGG, AND SOME RAISINS. SOME GIRLS AUTOMATICALLY STARTED COUGHING FROM ALL THE TANG POWDER FLOATING IN THE AIR. IT WAS WORSE THAN POWDER BUBBLE BATH.
I DON'T GET HOW THIS IS EVEN SPOSTO MIX TOGETHER.
COME ON! HOLD THE BOWL BETTER!
I'M HOLDIN' IT PERFECT. YOU JUST DON'T KNOW HOW TO STIR ANYTHING DECENT.

THEN, WHILE YOUR PARTNER IS PRE-HEATING THE OVEN AND GREASING THE COOKIE SHEET, YOU CUT THE CRUSTS OFF SOME BREAD. MY PARTNER WAS MARLYS WHO DIDN'T LISTEN WHEN MRS. VORICE SAID ALWAYS CHECK INSIDE THE OVEN BEFORE YOU TURN IT ON. IT'S MAINLY BECAUSE OF THAT OUR TANGY BREAKFAST SQUARES MAINLY HAD THE FLAVOR OF A BURNT UP RUBBER ERASER.
HOW WAS I SUPPOSED TO KNOW, MAN?
JUST AS IMPORTANT AS THE FLAVOR IS THE PRESENTATION OF THE FOOD. MRS. VORICE SAID WE MUST ALWAYS STRIVE TO MAKE OUR MEALS LOOK ATTRACTIVELY BEAUTIFUL. BUT YOU KNOW WITH TANGY BREAKFAST SQUARES I JUST DON'T THINK THERE'S ANY WAY.
I JUST DON'T THINK THAT CUTTING THEM UP INTO THE SHAPE OF THE CROSS IS REALLY GONNA HELP.
YOU WATCH. NO ONE GIVES ANYTHING LESS THAN A B- TO THE SHAPE OF THE CROSS

GUM OF MYSTERY
BY LYNDA BARRY WITH LISA JARRETT and BRENDA KIDDER © 1988
WE HAD AN EVIL MYSTERY GOING ON AT THE COAT ROOM. A SECRET JUVENILE DELINQUENT WAS PUTTING CHEWED UP GUM IN THE UNDERARMS OF EVERYONE'S COATS. WHAT A BAD CITIZEN.
AAUGH!
MISS MARTLES!
EEUH!
OH MAN!
DANG!
BOTH ARMS!
MRS. MARTLES! HE HAS STRUCK AGAIN!

THE THREE MAIN SUSPECTS WERE MY COUSIN MARLYS, KENNETH WATFORD, AND THAT NEW BOY, DEWEY-SOMETHING-IN-SPANISH.
MARLYS.
MAIN EVIDENCE:
IN A GUM WRAPPER CHAIN CONTEST WITH ESTHER COX FROM ROOM 9. HAS TO DO SOMETHING WITH EXTRA GUM. SHE'S SAYS SHES THE QUEEN OF ALL GUM.
KENNETH WATFORD
MAIN EVIDENCE:
ALWAYS TRYING TO GET ATTENTION, THROWS DIRT CLODS AT CARS, SPITS, PLAYS WITH HIS GUM. STRETCHES IT OUT OF HIS MOUTH, PUTS IT ON HIS FACE.
DEWEY M.
MAIN EVIDENCE:
HE'S NEW AND RUNS AROUND LIKE A WILD INDIAN AND TALKS OUT OF TURN AND ALWAYS ACTS LIKE HE HAS TO PEE. ALWAYS HAS CHICLETS.

WE EVEN HAD TO HAVE A DISCUSSION GROUP ABOUT IT BY SITTING IN INDIAN STYLE ON THE FLOOR AND RAISING OUR HANDS ABOUT "DISRESPECTING OTHER PEOPLE'S PRIVATE PROPERTY" AND "WHY GUM IS INSULTING."
1. Rude
2. Makes a mess
3. Tooth Decay
4. Unsightly
5. Waste of time
6. Disturbing
7.
ANYONE ELSE?
COME ON, CLASS, MISS MARTLE'S DOESN'T HAVE ALL DAY TO SPEND ON THIS SUBJECT.
CAN YOU BELIEVE IT WAS PAMMY LYONS THE WHOLE TIME? OUR QUIETEST, MOST SMARTEST GIRL OF THE CLASS WITH GLASSES WHO NEVER TALKS? WELL IT TURNS OUT THAT JUST BECAUSE SOMEONE IS SHY AND GETS ALL STRAIGHT A'S DOES NOT MEAN THEY WON'T PUT WADS OF GUM IN YOUR ARM PITS.
PAMMY, WE ARE ALL WAITING TO HEAR WHY YOU DID THIS, AREN'T WE CLASS?
PAMMY?
VALUABLE CLASS TIME IS BEING WASTED.
WOULD YOU RATHER TELL IT TO THE PRINCIPAL?
PAMMY?
WE CAN ARRANGE THAT.

THIS VASE
BY LYNDA BARRY © 1987
IT WAS WINDY AND POURING RAIN THE AFTERNOON OF FRIDAY OUR ART PERIOD. THE HARDEST RAIN YOU EVER SAW. YOU KNOW WHEN YOU SIT THERE AT YOUR DESK AND IT'S LIKE TONS OF BBs ARE JUST POUNDING OFF THE WINDOWS?
WE WERE ON CLAY. THE COIL METHOD. EVERYONE WAS ROLLING OUT THEIR MILLION LITTLE SNAKES CURLING THEM AROUND AND AROUND ON TOP OF EACH OTHER. AND THE RECORD PLAYER WAS GOING. WHAT WAS THAT SONG? THAT ONE ART PERIOD SONG?

EVEN WITH THE LIGHTS ON, OUR ROOM WAS DARK AND ALL THE DESKS WERE GANGED UP TOGETHER AND I KEPT STARING AT MY HANDS ON THE CLAY GOING BACK AND FORTH, BACK AND FORTH LIKE A PURE HYPNOTISER.

I WAS ROLLING THE CLAY WHEN MY TEACHER BENT DOWN AND PUT HER WARM HAND ON MY SHOULDER AND I DIDN'T STOP.
YOU KNOW HOW SOMETHING CAN FEEL SO PERFECT YOU CAN'T EVEN BLINK?
THAT WAS THE DAY I MADE THIS VASE FOR YOU.

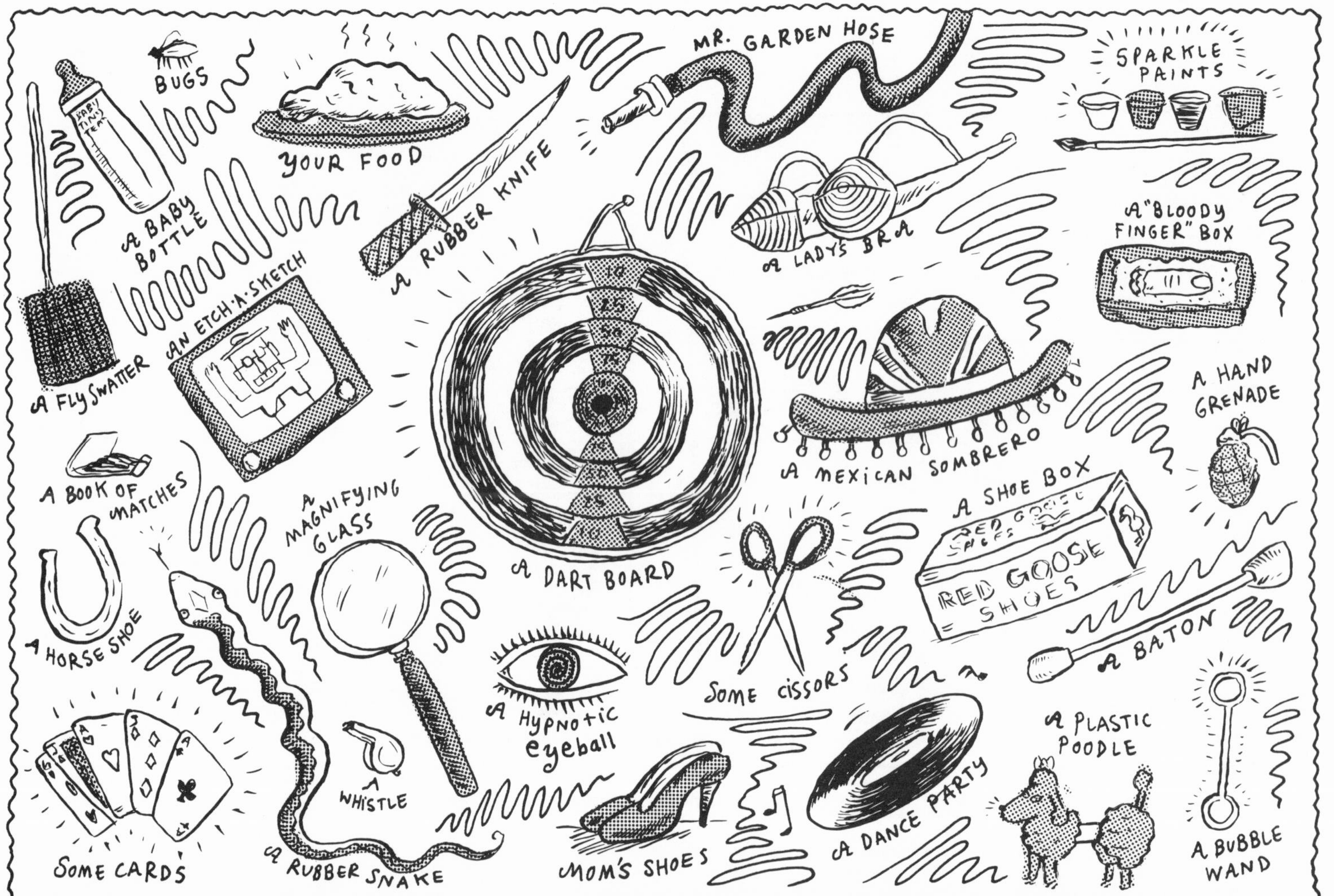
BUGS
YOUR FOOD
MR. GARDEN HOSE
SPARKLE PAINTS
A BABY BOTTLE
A RUBBER KNIFE
A LADY'S BRA
A "BLOODY FINGER" BOX
A FLY SWATTER
AN ETCH-A-SKETCH
A DART BOARD
A MEXICAN SOMBRERO
A HAND GRENADE
A BOOK OF MATCHES
A MAGNIFYING GLASS
A SHOE BOX
RED GOOSE SHOES
RED GOOSE SHOES
A HORSE SHOE
SOME CISSORS
A BATON
A Hypnotic eyeball
A WHISTLE
A PLASTIC POODLE
A BUBBLE WAND
SOME CARDS
A RUBBER SNAKE
MOM'S SHOES
A DANCE PARTY

PLAY
A BALLOON
AN INTERESTING STICK
A FLASHLIGHT
A HARMONICA
A BALL
CAPS
A RED WAGON
LITTLE FISHIES
A TRAFFIC CONE
A TROLL DOLL
A PLASTIC DINOSAUR
A GUN
A TANK
A BARBIE

PETS in our LIVES
BY LYNDA ~~BUSHMILLER~~ BARRY © 1987
Part One: REPTILES
WE HAD A COUSIN COME FROM IDAHO ONE TIME BY THE NAME OF MELTON AND HE BROUGHT HIS PET SNAKE CALLED "JOHNNY QUEST THE 2nd". JOHNNY QUEST THE FIRST DIED FROM EATING A WHOLE ROLL OF LIFE SAVERS ACCORDING TO MELTON WHO WAS A MAJOR LIAR.
WE EACH GOT A TURN AT HOLDING JOHNNY QUEST THE 2ND BY THE TAIL AND IF YOU HAVE NEVER HELD A SNAKE BEFORE, WELL, IT IS TOTALLY WORTH IT. THE SAD PART IS THAT ONLY CERTAIN KINDS OF MOMS WILL LET YOU HAVE A SNAKE AND OURS WAS NOT ONE OF THEM.
C'MON YOU GUYS WATCH ME! I WATCHED YOU WHEN YOU HELD HIM!
WATCH ME!
WATCH ME OR I'M TELLIN'!

IT TURNED OUT MELTON'S MOM WAS NOT A FRIEND TO SNAKES EITHER AND HAD A FIT WHEN SHE CAUGHT MELTON SHOWING OFF HIS SNAKE AND FOUND OUT SHE DROVE CLEAR FROM IDAHO WITH A SNAKE IN THE CAR. SHE SAID IF THAT SNAKE HAD GOTTEN LOOSE SHE WOULD HAVE DROVE STRAIGHT INTO A TREE AND THEY'D ALL BE DEAD AND HOW WOULD MELTON LIKE THAT FOR A CHANGE?
ANSWER ME!
MELTON HAD TO LET HIS SNAKE GO IN THE STICKERS IN OUR ALLEY AND EVEN THOUGH HE WAS SOMETHING LIKE 13, HE CRIED. HE SAID NOBODY WOULD LIKE HIM ANYMORE WITHOUT THAT SNAKE WHICH WAS TRUE. WITHOUT HIS SNAKE MELTON WAS NOTHING BUT REGULAR. THAT NIGHT WE ALL SNUCK OVER TO THE STICKERS AND MELTON WHISPERED "HERE BOY. HERE JOHNNY." I TOLD HIM I READ WHERE SNAKES CAN'T HEAR, AND HE TURNED AROUND AND SLUGGED ME.
DANG, MELTON!
I CAN'T HELP IT IF I KNOW SCIENCE.

PETS in OUR LIVES
BY LYNDA BARRY ©1987.
PART 2: SOME MORE REPTILES
IT WAS A GREAT DAY THE DAY WE GOT OUR TURTLES AND THEIR GORGEOUS HOME CALLED TURTLE ISLAND. WE GOT THEM AT THE WOOLWORTHS AND IT TOOK A LONG TIME TO PICK OUT THE PERFECT ONES OUT OF ABOUT TEN THOUSAND.
LADY!
THAT'S THE WRONG ONE!
NOT THAT ONE!
THE OTHER ONE!
THAT'S NOT IT!
THEY'RE ALL EXACTLY THE SAME.

TURTLE ISLAND WAS A DREAM HOUSE. IT CAME WITH A PLASTIC PALM TREE AND A PLACE TO SWIM AND A PLACE TO JUST GOOF OFF. WE EXPECTED OUR TURTLES TO GOOF OFF A LOT MORE THAN THEY DID THOUGH.
MINE JUST KIND OF MOVED AGAIN.
I WONDER CAN YOU TRAIN THEM.

MY BROTHER INVENTED THE GAME CALLED ESCAPE FROM TURTLE ISLAND AND HIS TURTLE NAMED HARRY MOSCOW WAS THE STAR AND MY TURTLE NAMED QUEENIE WAS HIS GLAMOROUS ASSISTANT. ALL IT WAS WAS THEM CRAWLING ON THE KITCHEN FLOOR WHILE MY BROTHER SANG GOLDFINGER.
♪GOLD FINGA!♪ NUH-NUH-NUH! ♪ HE'S THE MAN, THE MAN WITH THE ♪GOLD FINGA! ♪ NA-NAH-NA HE'S THE MAN, THE MAN WITH THE ♪ GOLD FINGA!

OUR TURTLES STAYED AT OUR AUNT SYLVIA'S WHEN WE WENT ON VACATION AND THAT WAS THE END OF OUR TURTLES. OUR MOM TOLD US LATER AUNT SYLVIA NEVER WAS THAT GOOD WITH ANIMALS. YOU WOULD LIKE TO KNOW WHAT HAPPENED TO OUR PETS BUT NO ONE WOULD TELL US. AUNT SYLVIA JUST GAVE US EACH A DOLLAR AND OUR EMPTY TURTLE ISLAND WITH A BIG CRACK IN IT.
YOU JUST WAIT 'TIL SHE GETS A TURTLE, MAN.

FOUND A PEANUT
BY LYNDA BARRY ©1987
THAT SONG, "FOUND A PEANUT" WAS ABOUT OUR NUMBER ONE SONG. IT WAS A FUN SONG TO SING.
OK NOW WATCH MY MAGIC HAND WHILE I SING SO YOU CAN FOLLOW THE NOTES.
NO MAN, JUST TELL ME THE PART THAT GOES AFTER "CRACKED IT OPEN, IT WAS ROTTEN."
FIRST WATCH MY MAGIC HAND
FORGET IT, MAN. WATCH MY MAGIC BUTT.
I'M TELLIN'!
MARLYS MADE A BIG DEAL ABOUT HOW SHE KNEW ALL THE WORDS. WE WANTED HER TO TELL US BUT WE DIDN'T WANT TO HAVE TO WATCH HER STAND ON A CHAIR DOING THAT MAGIC HAND THING WHICH SHE LEARNED FROM WATCHING MISS DORIS ON SCHOOL T.V. THE GOAL OF MARLYS'S LIFE WAS TO BE THE STAR OF HER OWN SHOW LIKE ON MISS DORIS TIME.
MARLYS PARTICIPATING WITH HER IDOL MISS DORIS
(CLOSE UP OF MISS DORIS ON TV)
MAGIC HAND
MY HOME'S IN MONTANA, I WEAR A BANDANA

THE WAY WE FINALLY ENDED UP KNOWING THE WORDS WAS BY SNEAKING LOOKS THROUGH THE CRACK IN THE DOOR, SEEING MARLYS DO THE WHOLE MISS DORIS SHOW BY STANDING ON THE TOILET AND WATCHING HERSELF IN THE MIRROR. AFTER A WHILE WE DIDN'T EVEN CARE ABOUT THE SONG "FOUND A PEANUT" ALTHOUGH IT WAS MARLYS'S SPECIALTY. TURNS OUT WE JUST LIKED WATCHING MARLYS. SHE SHOULD GO IN A TALENT SHOW.
GOOD MORNING BOYS AND GIRLS! I'M SO GLAD YOU'RE HERE TODAY! LET'S SING "I'M A LITTLE TEA POT" SHALL WE? GOOD. WATCH MY MAGIC HAND! REMEMBER DON'T STICK YOUR BOTTOMS OUT SO MUCH OR YOU'LL LOOK LIKE A STUPID IDIOT, OK? NO WAIT A SEC. LET'S SING "DRILL YE TERRIERS DRILL" NO, LET'S DO "FOUND A PEANUT" IS EVERYBODY READY? MR. PITCHPIPE, WILL YOU GIVE US OUR NOTE? ONE TWO THREE

WE SECRETLY KNEW THAT MARLYS SECRETLY KNEW WE WERE WATCHING BUT NOBODY EVER SAID NOTHING UNTIL THE TIME MARLYS TRIED TO DO THAT GO GO DANCING SONG AND FELL OFF THE TOILET AND THE SEAT CAME FLYING OFF AND SHE SPRAINED HER MAGIC ARM AND GOT SOME MAGIC BRUISES. HER MOM CAME RUNNING IN AND SPANKED EVERYONE OF US AND WANTED TO KNOW WHY WE HAD TO LEARN EVERYTHING THE HARD WAY? ESPECIALLY MARLYS.

THE EL RANCHO
BY LYNDA BARRY ©1987
THE FIRST RULE OF GOING TO A DRIVE-IN MOVIE IS YOU HAVE TO WEAR YOUR PAJAMAS. IT'S O.K. BECAUSE EVERYBODY LIKES RUNNING AROUND OUTSIDE IN PAJAMAS. IT MAKES YOU FEEL VERY FRIENDLY TOWARDS YOUR NEIGHBORS.
HI
HI
WE GOT THE EXACT SAME PAJAMAS
I KNOW
YOUR MOM BUY THEM AT WIGWAM?
YUP.
SAME HERE.

THE NEXT RULE IS IT'S O.K. TO CLIMB ON TOP OF THE CAR BUT NO JUMPING. ALSO, BE SURE TO ASK PERMISSION FIRST BEFORE YOU JUMP ON THE CARS OF OTHERS.
WHY NOT, MISTER?
WE'LL BE REALLY QUIET.

THE THIRD RULE IS WHEN THEY SHOW THE MOVIE OF THE DANCING HOT DOGS AND CANDY DON'T CLIMB DOWN OFF THE CAR AND ASK AUNT AGNES FOR MONEY. ALSO WHEN THEY SHOW THE DANCING HAMBURGER WITH "MELLOW CHEESE" STAND ON TOP OF THE CAR AND YELL "SMELLO!" AND IF YOU'RE MY BROTHER START DANCING LIKE THE HAMBURGER UNTIL AUNT AGNES MAKES YOU QUIT.
OUR SNAKS 'N' TREETS ARE SURE TO PLEASE
I SAID KNOCK IT OFF!
HAM-BER-GERS WITH SMELLO CHEESE

ALSO: BE CAREFUL WHEN YOU GO TO THE RESTROOM OR YOU MIGHT MISS THE PART WHEN MEDUSA GETS HER HEAD CHOPPED OFF. AND IF YOU GET SCARED JUST KEEP SAYING "IT'S NOT BLOOD IT'S KETCHUP." AND YOU BETTER BE BACK TO THE CAR BY "THE END", THATS ALL AUNT AGNES HAS TO SAY.
I TOLD YOU, CRYING ABOUT IT IS NOT GOING TO PUT THAT MEDUSA'S HEAD BACK ON HER BODY JUST SO YOU CAN SEE IT GET WACKED OFF AGAIN.
IT'S YOUR OWN FAULT YOU MISSED IT AND BESIDES, THAT MOVIE WILL BE ON T.V. BY NEXT YEAR.

LOVE ADVENTURE
LYNDA "I'M A HOG FOR YOU" BARRY © 1987
THERE WERE THESE VERY POPULAR BUSHES IN OUR NEIGHBORHOOD WHERE PRACTICALLY EVERYONE ON THE PLANET GOT THEIR FIRST KISS. ME AND DEENA SAID WE GOT OURS THERE TOO BY SOMEBODY'S COUSIN FROM IDAHO BUT IT WAS A LIE. WE HAD NEVER KISSED NO ONE.
NO ONE'S EVER GONNA KISS US MAN. AND NO BODY EVEN BELIEVES US ABOUT THAT GUY FROM IDAHO EITHER. WHO'D EVER KISS A GUY FROM IDAHO?
AT LEAST WE'RE NOT SLUTS.
SO?
CREEM

WE TRIED TO COPY THE SENSUOUS LOOKS THAT MAKE A MAN HYPNOTISED AS SEEN ON T.V. AND IN OUR OPINION WE GOT THOSE LOOKS PERFECTED.

WHEN I FINALLY GOT MY FIRST KISS AND DEENA GOT HERS WE COULD NOT HELP BUT FEEL A CERTAIN ELEMENT OF DISAP-POINTMENT. WE COULD NOT EXPLAIN EXACTLY WHERE THIS FEELING CAME FROM AND NEITHER DID WE KNOW THAT WE WOULD SPEND THE NEXT TWENTY YEARS TRYING TO FIND OUT.
WELL HOW COME AFTER THEY KISSED US THEY START ACTING LIKE THEY DON'T EVEN LIKE US ANYMORE?
BECAUSE GUYS ARE STUPID.
THEN HOW COME WE STILL LIKE THEM?
I DON'T KNOW YET.

WE TRIED THEM OUT AT PARTIES BUT AS IT TURNED OUT THE GUYS OUR AGE WERE NOT AS SOPHISTICATED AS WE WERE.
YOU GUYS BEEN AT THE AQUARIUM OR SOMETHING?
I DON'T GET IT.
IS THIS SOME KIND OF DARE?

IF YOU WANT TO BUY CANDY
BY LYNDA BARRY ©1987
NUMBER ONE, BUY YOUR CANDY AT FRED'S NOT AT BLUMA'S. BLUMAS GOTS THE CANDY IN A GLASS CASE AND HE WON'T LET YOU EVEN TOUCH IT UNTIL YOU PAY. EVERYBODY JUST HATES BLUMA. HIS STORE SMELLS LIKE LYSOL.
YOU TAKE TOO LONG! OUTSIDE UNTIL YOU KNOW WHAT YOU WANT!
MAN I'M JUST LOOKING! CAN'T A GUY EVEN LOOK?

FRED'S GOTS THE GOOD CANDY AND YOU CAN PICK IT UP AND PUT IT BACK AND TAKE YOUR TIME MAKING YOUR DECISIONS. BLUMA'S GOTS OLD CHOCOLATE SANTAS WAY UNTIL JULY 4TH AND HE DON'T EVEN REDUCE THE PRICE. BLUMA WEARS A HAIRNET. A MAN WEARS A HAIRNET.
YOU KIDS!
YOU THINK I AM JOKING YOU?! OUT! OUT! OUT!
YOU WANT ME TO BOCKLE YOUR HEAD!?
HAIR IN EARS

ALSO BLUMA RUNS OUTSIDE AFTER YOU YELLING WHERE DO THE WRAPPERS GO! WHERE DO THE WRAPPERS GO! FRED JUST SITS THERE SMOKING. FRED DON'T HARDLY MOVE FOR NOTHING NOT EVEN IF YOUR BIKE BASHES AGAINST HIS WINDOW WHEN YOU LEAN IT DOWN. BUT BLUMA DON'T LET NO BIKES EVEN TOUCH HIS STORE. HE'LL HIT YOU WITH THE FLY SWATTER, HE DON'T CARE.
FRED
FRED HOW MUCH FOR THESE MONSTER CARDS
10¢
CREEPY MONSTER
BLUMA
NO BIKES!
NO BIKES!
NO BIKES!
WHO MADE THIS GARBAGE!

THE ONLY THING ABOUT FRED'S IS THAT IT CAN MAKE YOU SORT OF SAD BECAUSE OF THE WAY HE NEVER TALKS. AT LEAST WITH BLUMA HE'LL CHASE AFTER YOU AND YOU GET TO SEE HIS GIANT BUTT AND LEGS. NO ONE IN THE WORLD HAS EVER SEEN THE LEGS OF FRED. OUR MOM SAYS HE DON'T TALK BECAUSE OF HIS WIFE LEFT HIM. WHAT A DUMB STUPID LADY.
HI FRED! HOW ARE YOU FRED.
Hi.
Hi FRED.
HI AND EVERYTHING
HI FRED

A BIRD TO SING
BY LYNDA BARRY © 1987
I'M TELLING THIS DUMB STORY MYSELF. MY NAME IS ARNOLD AND I SHOT A BIRD.

IT FELL AND I SAW IT FALL AND I JUST STOOD THERE SAYING REALLY I MISSED. REALLY IT JUST FLEW AWAY.

THAT BIRD IS BARELY MOVING, LAYING SIDEWAYS IN THE LEAVES, BREATHING ABOUT A MILLION MILES AN HOUR.
EVEN WHEN YOU AIM AT SOMETHING, IT CAN STILL BE A TOTAL ACCIDENT, CAN'T IT?

AT NIGHT I KEEP SAYING BIG DEAL, BIG DEAL, IT'S JUST A STUPID BIRD. BUT IT TURNS OUT THERE'S NO SUCH THING.
IF YOU TELL ANYONE, I'LL BASH YOUR HEAD IN.

MOVIE REVIEW OF:
SUPER KUNG-FU DUDE
AS TOLD AND PART-DRAWN BY DEWEY MUÑOZ
TO: LYNDA BARRY ©
OK. SO I WENT WITH OSCAR FUNG AND HIS MOM, MRS. FUNG, TO THE CHINESE MOVIES, RIGHT? AND WE SAW THIS KUNG-FU MOVIE IN TOTAL CHINESE THAT OSCAR SAID THE TITLE OF WAS "SUPER KUNG-FU DUDE" BUT OBVIOUSLY THAT'S NOT THE REAL NAME OF IT.
OK?

SO THE SUPER KUNG-FU GUY IS WALKING, THEN 3 BANK ROBBERS RUN OUT AND HE TRIES TO STOP THEM SO THE MAIN DIA-BOLICAL ROBBER HURLS A CHINESE COIN AT HIM AND IT GOES RIGHT INTO HIS STOMACH. LIKE ACTUALLY ENGRAVED ON HIS STOMACH, RIGHT? THE METAL PART.
MAIN DIABOLICAL ROBBER
THE BANK
THE COIN
CLOSE-UP OF COIN IN HIS STOMACH
EVIL ASSISTANTS GETTING AWAY
SUPER KUNG-FU DUDE

SO THEN THE ROBBERS ESCAPE TO THEIR SWAMP HIDE-A-WAY AND THE KUNG-FU MAN BUILDS HIS MUSCLES AND CAN SUDDENLY FLY 50 FEET IN THE AIR AND HE KEEPS ASKING EVERYONE "TELL ME WHERE IS LONG-LOW-FUNKY-TONGUE-DOW!" AND THE PEOPLE SAY "I DON'T KNOW" SO HIS EYEBROWS GO UP IN FURY AND HE SHOUTS "LIAR!" AND KARATE CHOPS THEM.
CHOP!
CHOP!
CHOP!

THEN HE FINDS THEM AND OPENS THE DOOR AND THE GIRL PRISONERS IN BIKINIS RUN OUT AND HE GETS IN A MASSIVE SWORD FIGHT AND HE STABS THE DIABOLICAL GUY IN THE STOMACH BUT THEN HE GETS STABBED IN THE EYEBALL AND THEY BOTH DIE AND THEY PLAY CHINESE MUSIC AND THEN THE END.

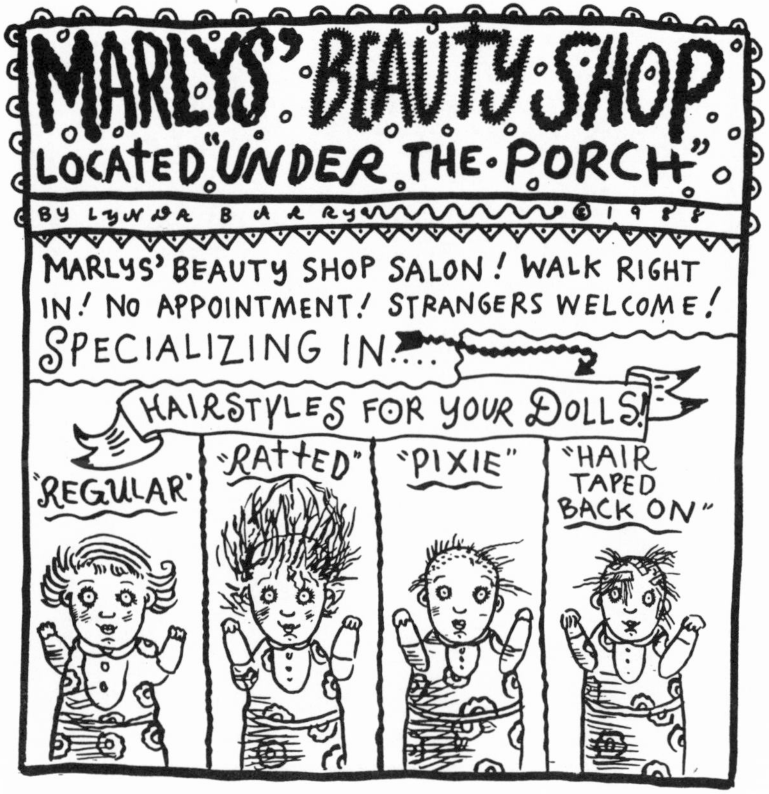
MARLYS' BEAUTY SHOP
LOCATED "UNDER THE PORCH"
BY LYNDA BARRY ©1988
MARLYS' BEAUTY SHOP SALON! WALK RIGHT IN! NO APPOINTMENT! STRANGERS WELCOME!
SPECIALIZING IN....
HAIRSTYLES FOR YOUR DOLLS!
"REGULAR"
"RATTED"
"PIXIE"
"HAIR TAPED BACK ON"

SPECIALIZING IN......
HAIRSTYLES FOR YOUR PETS!
NOW QUIT YOUR CRAZY FIDGETING!
CRAYOLA AND MASKING TAPE MANICURES!
DIRECTIONS: COLOR TAPE WITH RED. CUT PIECES OFF AND PUT THEM ON YOUR NAILS. IT'S PERFECTLY GORGEOUS!

SPECIALIZING IN.....
BEFORES AND AFTERS!
"NORMALLY"
"THANK-YOU, MARLYS"
CANDY CIGARETTE
EYEBROWS
GLAMOUROUS BLONDE FALL OF LIFELIKE HAIR YOU HAVE TO HOLD UP. (BELONGS TO MOM)
LIP STICK (ACTUAL)
PARIS STYLE EVENING GOWN IN REALITY THE SHOWER CURTAIN
ALLURING BEAUTY MARKS
WEARING TOILET WATER, HER ODOR IS IRRESISTABLE

SPECIALIZING IN.....
FABULOUS HAIR-DOS FOR YOU!
I DON'T THINK YOU SHOULD USE NO MORE HAIRSPRAY MARLYS. ONE CAN'S ENOUGH.
IT FEELS PRETTY FROZE.
IT'S ALMOST PERFECT.
AQUA NET

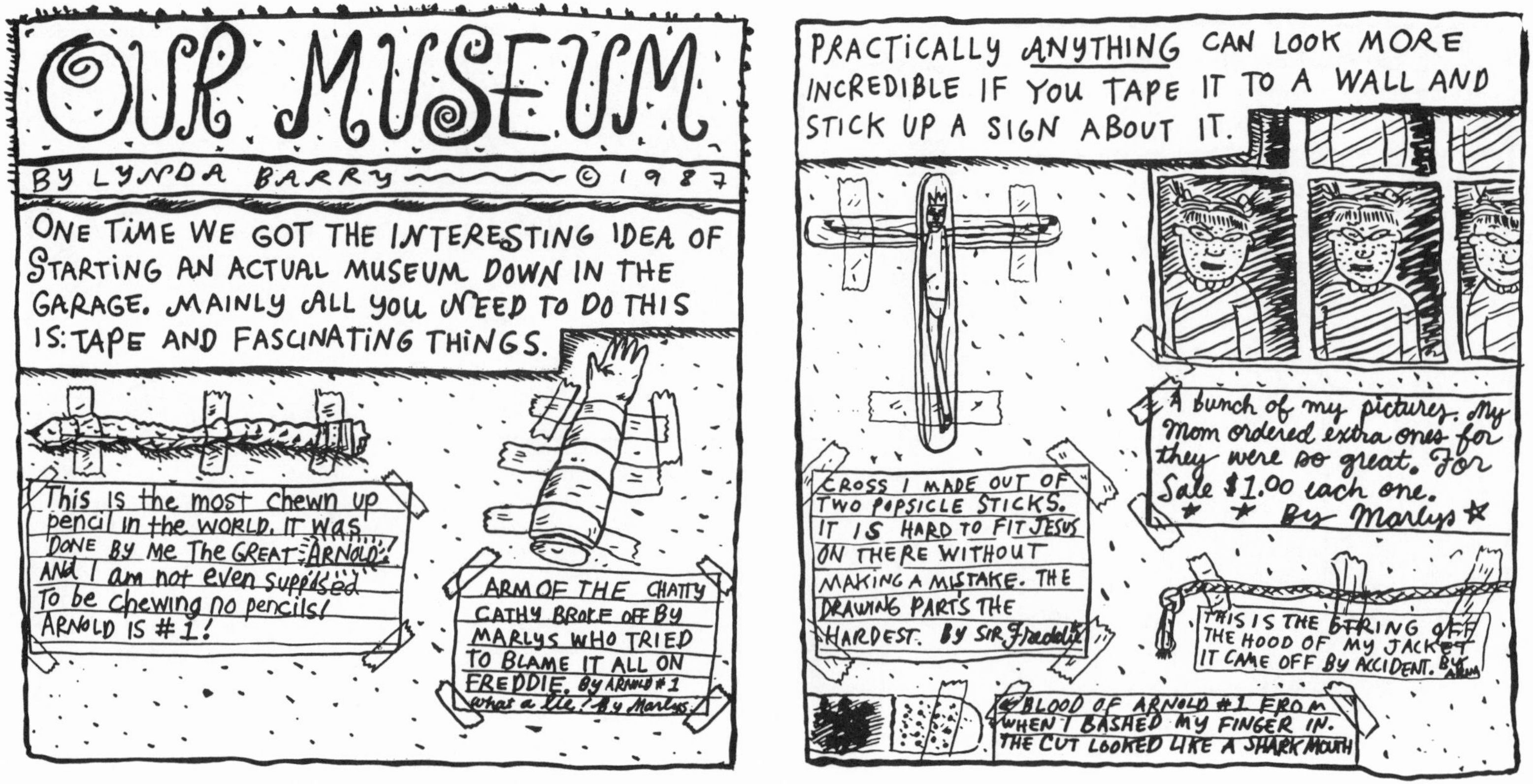
OUR MUSEUM
BY LYNDA BARRY ©1987
ONE TIME WE GOT THE INTERESTING IDEA OF STARTING AN ACTUAL MUSEUM DOWN IN THE GARAGE. MAINLY ALL YOU NEED TO DO THIS IS: TAPE AND FASCINATING THINGS.
This is the most chewn up pencil in the WORLD. IT WAS DONE BY ME The GREAT ARNOLD! And I am not even supposed to be chewing no pencils! ARNOLD IS #1!
ARM OF THE CHATTY CATHY BROKE OFF BY MARLYS WHO TRIED TO BLAME IT ALL ON FREDDIE. BY ARNOLD #1
what a lie! By Marlys
PRACTICALLY ANYTHING CAN LOOK MORE INCREDIBLE IF YOU TAPE IT TO A WALL AND STICK UP A SIGN ABOUT IT.
CROSS I MADE OUT OF TWO POPSICLE STICKS. IT IS HARD TO FIT JESUS ON THERE WITHOUT MAKING A MISTAKE. THE DRAWING PARTS THE HARDEST. By SIR Freddie
A bunch of my pictures. My Mom ordered extra ones for they were so great. For Sale $1.00 each one. ★ ★ By Marlys ★
THIS IS THE STRING OFF THE HOOD OF MY JACKET IT CAME OFF BY ACCIDENT. BY ARNOLD
BLOOD OF ARNOLD #1 FROM WHEN I BASHED MY FINGER IN. THE CUT LOOKED LIKE A SHARK MOUTH

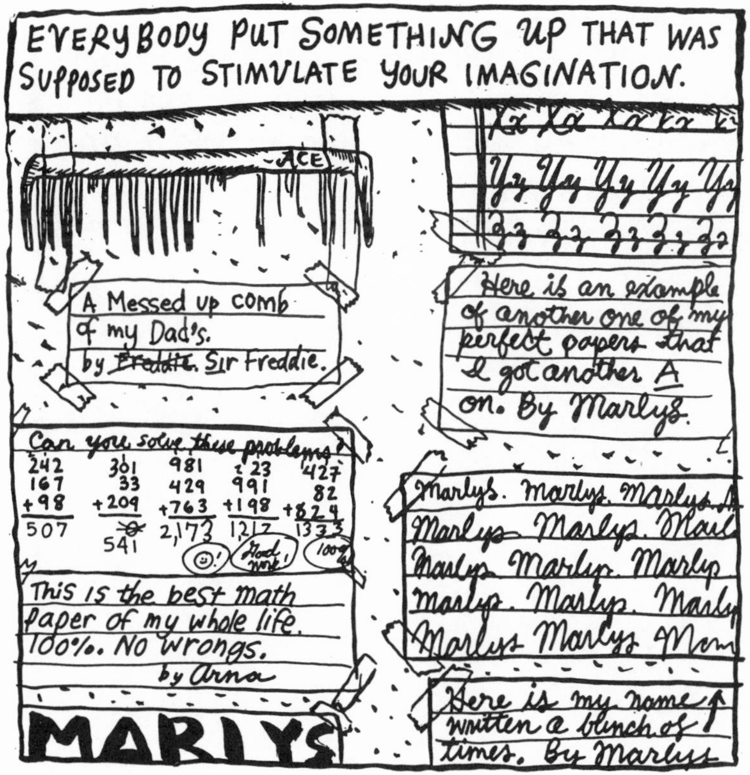
EVERYBODY PUT SOMETHING UP THAT WAS SUPPOSED TO STIMULATE YOUR IMAGINATION.
ACE
A Messed up comb of my Dad's. by ~~Freddie.~~ Sir Freddie.
Can you solve these problems?
242 167 +98 507
301 33 +209 541
981 429 +763 2,173
This is the best math paper of my whole life. 100%. No wrongs. by Arna
MARLYS
Here is an example of another one of my perfect papers that I got another A on. By Marlys.
Marlys. Marlys. Marlys.
Here is my name written a bunch of times. By Marlys

WE COULD HAVE KEPT GOING BUT WE RAN OUT OF TAPE. WE TRIED ELMER'S GLUE BUT IT TAKES TOO LONG TO JUST STAND THERE AND HOLD IT UNTIL IT STICKS, YOU KNOW?
THIS is Marlys' DOLL
MARLYS
C'MON YOU GUYS! SOME ONE ELSE TAKE A TURN AT THIS! NO FAIR!
MY ARMS ARE GETTING DEAD!
YOU GUYS! WHERE YA GOIN'?!! I'M TELLIN'! MOM! MOM!

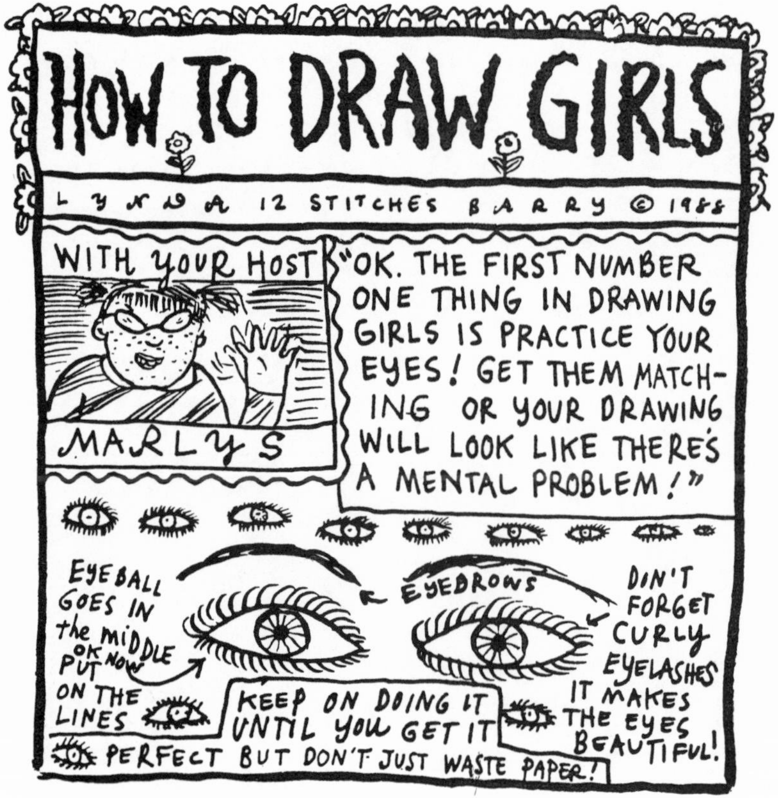
HOW TO DRAW GIRLS
LYNDA 12 STITCHES BARRY © 1988
WITH YOUR HOST
MARLYS
"OK. THE FIRST NUMBER ONE THING IN DRAWING GIRLS IS PRACTICE YOUR EYES! GET THEM MATCHING OR YOUR DRAWING WILL LOOK LIKE THERE'S A MENTAL PROBLEM!"
EYEBALL GOES IN the MIDDLE
EYEBROWS
DON'T FORGET CURLY EYELASHES
OK NOW PUT ON THE LINES
KEEP ON DOING IT UNTIL YOU GET IT PERFECT BUT DON'T JUST WASTE PAPER!
IT MAKES THE EYES BEAUTIFUL!

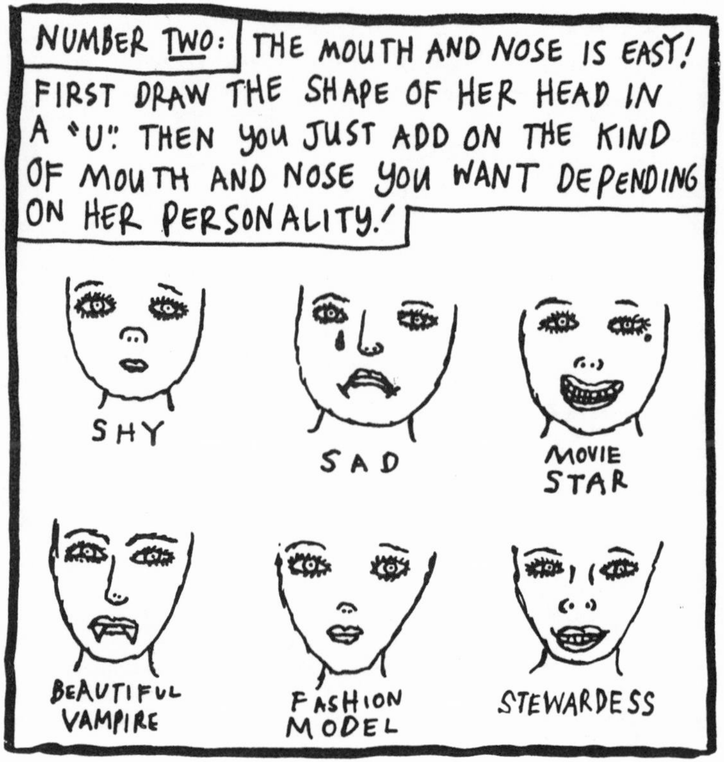
NUMBER TWO:
THE MOUTH AND NOSE IS EASY! FIRST DRAW THE SHAPE OF HER HEAD IN A "U". THEN YOU JUST ADD ON THE KIND OF MOUTH AND NOSE YOU WANT DEPENDING ON HER PERSONALITY!
SHY
SAD
MOVIE STAR
BEAUTIFUL VAMPIRE
FASHION MODEL
STEWARDESS

NUMBER THREE: WHAT ABOUT HER HAIR?
THERES A LOT OF HAIR-DOS FOR HER TO HAVE! THERES A LOT OF STYLES!
PEEK-A-BOO
A BEAUTY PAGEANT
INDIAN PRINCESS
WEE! WEE!
A FRANCE LADY
A GORGEOUS FLIP
RATTED BUBBLE

NUMBER FOUR: THE HARDEST PART: YOU HAVE TO DRAW HER WHOLE BODY AND THIS IS WHERE YOU CAN WRECK EVERYTHING SO BE CAREFUL! MY SECRET IS: DRAW A LONG BEAUTIFUL DRESS AND HER HOLDING FLOWERS AND DON'T FORGET SOME ELEGANT ACCESSORIES!
A CROWN ALWAYS LOOKS LOVELY.
FLOWERS CAN HIDE HANDS THAT'S TOO HARD TO DRAW
PUT IN BIRDS
DRAW ON A WATCH
HER PURSE. IT'S IMPORTANT
DECORATE THE DRESS PLEASE
DRAW A TREE HERE AND SHE CAN LOOK LIKE SHES IN THE FOREST
SHOES CAN STICK OUT
THE END BY MARLYS

SMOKING WORLD
BY LYNDA BARRY
with your host, Marlys!
CIGARS? CIGARETTES? TIPARILLOS?
WINSTON TASTES GOOD LIKE A CIGARETTE SHOULD!
SHOW US YOUR LARK PACK!
STEP UP TO DUTCH MASTERS AND SMILE, BROTHER, SMILE!
I'D RATHER FIGHT THAN SWITCH!
A SILLY MILLIMETER LONGER!
TAKE A PUFF, IT'S SPRINGTIME
ENJOY THE ELEGANT SMOKING PLEASURES OF RAW SPAGHETTI, BUT WATCH OUT BECAUSE IT BREAKS EASY AND IF YOU GET TOO MUCH SPIT ON THE END, IT TURNS WHITE AND BENDS.
RED AND BLACK LICORICE IS LOVELY BUT IT ALSO HAS THE BENDING PROBLEM.
WHITE CRAYONS ARE GOOD WHEN YOU PEEL OFF THE PAPER AND PUT THE POINTED END IN YOUR MOUTH. LOOKS GENUINE!
WHITE PAPER STRAWS ARE NICE AND YOU CAN ACTUALLY LIGHT THE ENDS TO MAKE IT REALISTIC. DON'T LIGHT THE PLASTIC ONES, THOUGH, BECAUSE A WAD CAN MELT OFF AND LAND ON YOUR LEG AND YOU WILL RUN SCREAMING.

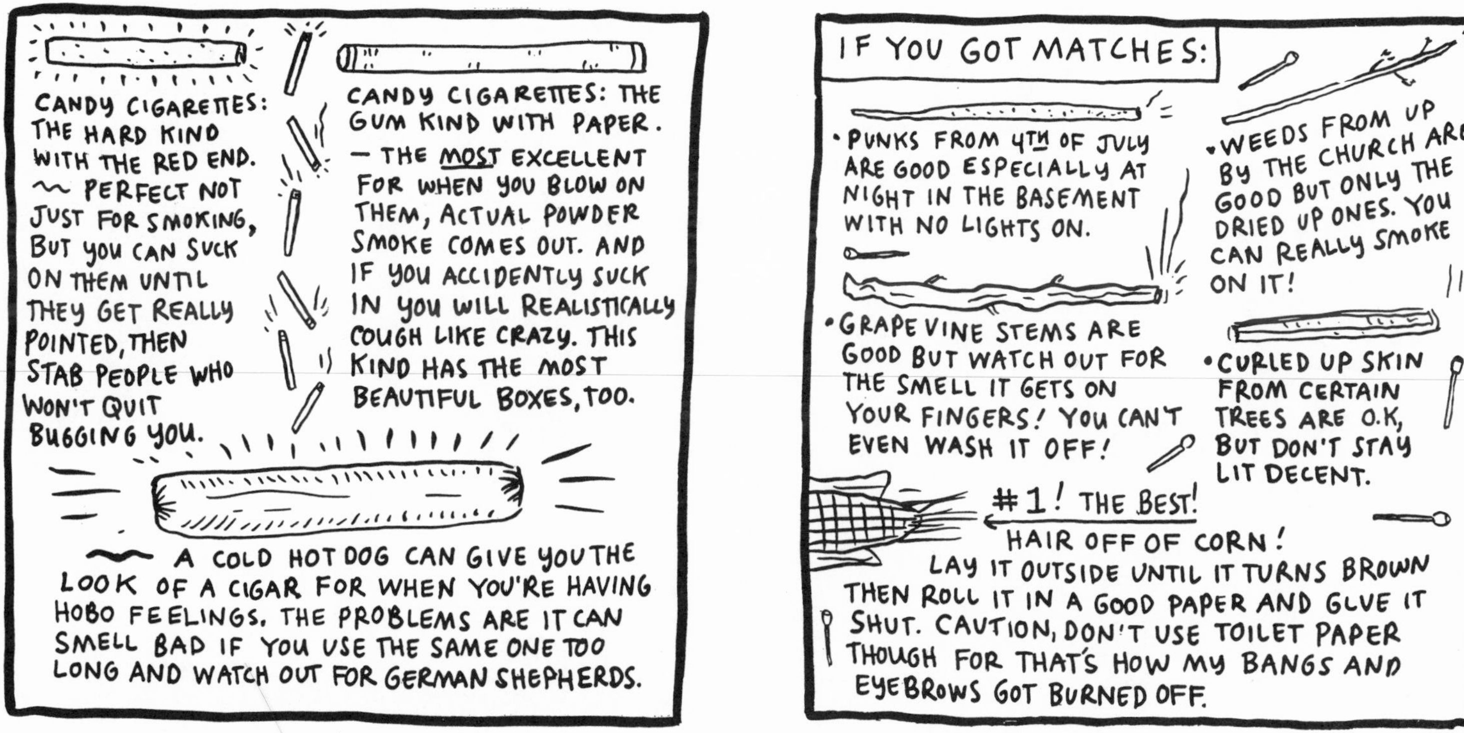
CANDY CIGARETTES: THE HARD KIND WITH THE RED END. ~ PERFECT NOT JUST FOR SMOKING, BUT YOU CAN SUCK ON THEM UNTIL THEY GET REALLY POINTED, THEN STAB PEOPLE WHO WON'T QUIT BUGGING YOU.
CANDY CIGARETTES: THE GUM KIND WITH PAPER. — THE MOST EXCELLENT FOR WHEN YOU BLOW ON THEM, ACTUAL POWDER SMOKE COMES OUT. AND IF YOU ACCIDENTLY SUCK IN YOU WILL REALISTICALLY COUGH LIKE CRAZY. THIS KIND HAS THE MOST BEAUTIFUL BOXES, TOO.
~ A COLD HOT DOG CAN GIVE YOU THE LOOK OF A CIGAR FOR WHEN YOU'RE HAVING HOBO FEELINGS. THE PROBLEMS ARE IT CAN SMELL BAD IF YOU USE THE SAME ONE TOO LONG AND WATCH OUT FOR GERMAN SHEPHERDS.
IF YOU GOT MATCHES:
• PUNKS FROM 4TH OF JULY ARE GOOD ESPECIALLY AT NIGHT IN THE BASEMENT WITH NO LIGHTS ON.
• WEEDS FROM UP BY THE CHURCH ARE GOOD BUT ONLY THE DRIED UP ONES. YOU CAN REALLY SMOKE ON IT!
• GRAPE VINE STEMS ARE GOOD BUT WATCH OUT FOR THE SMELL IT GETS ON YOUR FINGERS! YOU CAN'T EVEN WASH IT OFF!
• CURLED UP SKIN FROM CERTAIN TREES ARE O.K, BUT DON'T STAY LIT DECENT.
#1! THE BEST!
HAIR OFF OF CORN! LAY IT OUTSIDE UNTIL IT TURNS BROWN THEN ROLL IT IN A GOOD PAPER AND GLUE IT SHUT. CAUTION, DON'T USE TOILET PAPER THOUGH FOR THAT'S HOW MY BANGS AND EYEBROWS GOT BURNED OFF.

T-POLE
LYNDA · BARRY ©1988
IN MY COUSIN MARLYS'S BACK YARD WAS THE CLOTHES LINE T-POLE WHICH WE LOVED TO HANG UPSIDE DOWN ON. IN FACT, WE WERE BECOMING PURE EXPERTS AT IT.

IF YOU HOOK YOUR LEGS JUST RIGHT AND SWING, THERE'S THIS FEELING YOU CAN GET LIKE YOUR PANTS ARE ITCHING YOU IN THIS MOST PERFECTLY GORGEOUS WAY.

AND WHEN YOU LET YOUR ARMS HANG DOWN AND CLOSE YOUR EYELASHES SO THERE'S THE SPARKLING RAYS AND YOUR DOG COMES OVER AND LICKS YOUR HAND, WELL, HOW CAN YOU RESIST IT?

MY AUNT YELLS OUT THE WINDOW WATCH IT, THE BLOOD'S GONNA RUSH TO YOUR HEADS AND YOU'LL PASS OUT AND FALL OFF AND CRACK YOUR SKULLS, BUT ME AND MARLYS AGREE. IT WOULD STILL BE TOTALLY WORTH IT.

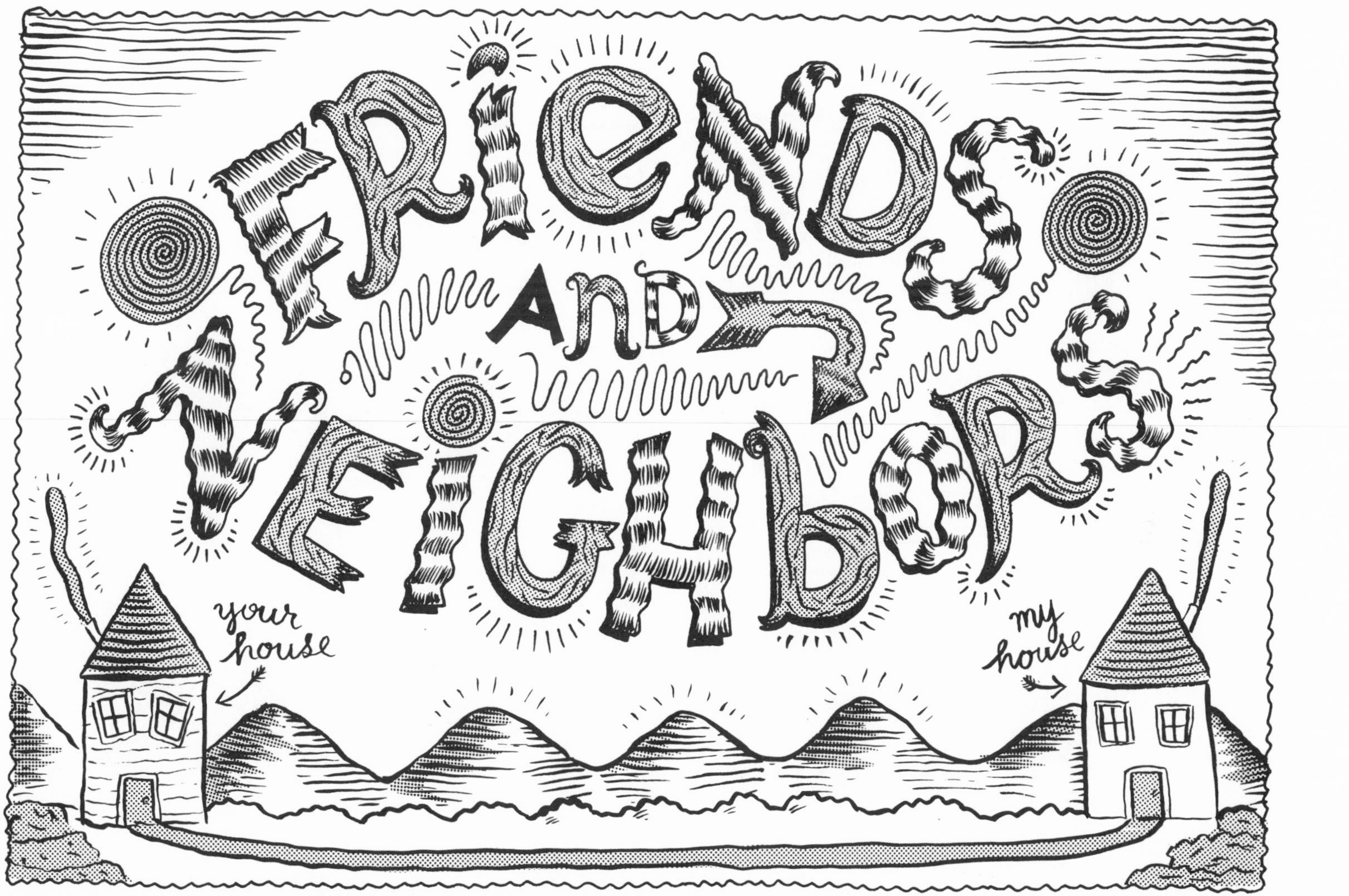
Friends and Neighbors
your house
my house

SMOKE, SMOKE, SMOKE
LYNDA BARRY tells JOHN MULLEN'S CIG STORY © 1988
MY FRIEND STEVE SHOVLIN SENT IN TWO BOX TOPS AND GOT MAILED A CHECK WITH JIMMY DURANTE'S FACE ON IT WORTH 50¢ WHICH HE CASHED UP AT THE CHINESE GROCERY STORE AND THEN WHEN NOBODY WAS WATCHING BOUGHT A PACK OF LUCKY STRIKES OUT OF THE CIGARETTE MACHINE.

WE WALKED UP TO WHERE THEY WERE BUILDING THE NEW CHURCH, TAKING TURNS HOLDING THE PACK IN OUR POCKETS. A POLICE CAR DROVE BY AND WE JUST ABOUT FAINTED. WE GOT TO THE MAIN DITCH AND JUMPED DOWN INTO IT. IT WAS JUST STARTING TO GET DARK.

WE LIGHTED THEM AND STEVE CLOSED HIS EYES AND SAID "AHH.... ALIVE WITH PLEASURE" AND THEN STARTED COUGHING SO BAD HE DROPPED HIS CIGARETTE AND GOT DIRT ALL OVER IT. WE COUGHED AND COUGHED AND FELT LIKE THROWING UP BUT AT LEAST IT WAS WORTH IT.

TO DESTROY THE EVIDENCE WE LIT THE REST OF THE CIGARETTES ONE BY ONE AND STUCK THEM INTO A DIRT PILE. IT WAS DARK AND THE ENDS WERE GLOWING ORANGE AND DOWN THE HILL WE COULD HEAR THE TRAIN GOING BY. WE SAT ON OUR HEELS NOT TALKING AND WATCHING THE CIGARETTES BURN AND ALL OF A SUDDEN I JUST KNEW STEVE WAS GOING TO BE MY BEST FRIEND FOR THE REST OF MY LIFE.

DRACULA
LYNDA BARRY ©1988
ON WARM NIGHTS AFTER IT WAS TOO DARK TO PLAY KICKBALL, WE WOULD GO TO MRS. VIDRINES AND ASK COULD WE PLEASE PLAY "I'M DRACULA" IN HER YARD. SHE WAS HARD OF HEARING SO SHE ALWAYS SAID YES.

SHE HAD TALL TALL GRASS AND SEVEN PLUM TREES YOU COULD HIDE IN LIKE CRAZY WHILE WHO EVER WAS "IT" FOR DRACULA LAID ON THE BACK PORCH COFFIN COUNTING TO 50 AND THEN SCREAMED OUT IN THE DARK "I'M COMING ALIVE!" WHICH WOULD MAKE YOU FEEL LIKE SUDDENLY PEEING.

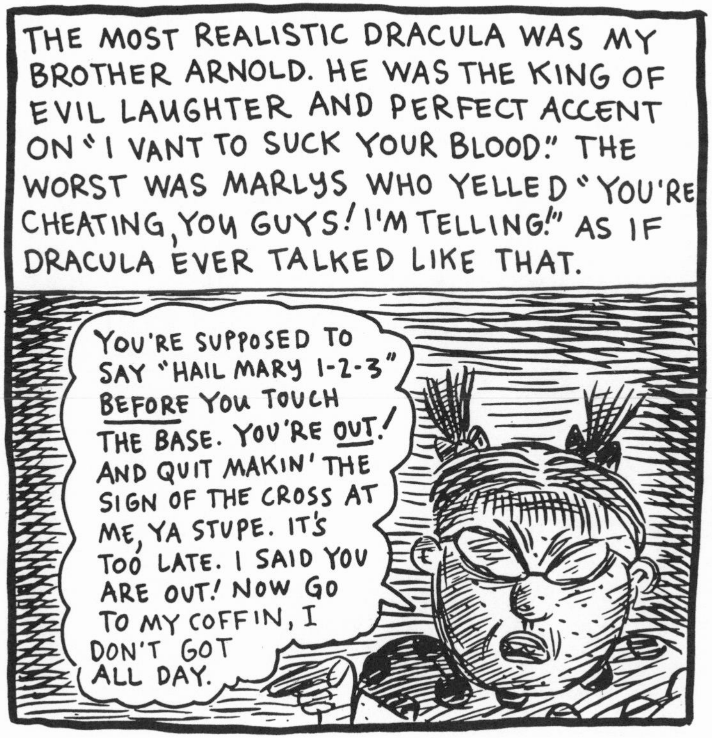
THE MOST REALISTIC DRACULA WAS MY BROTHER ARNOLD. HE WAS THE KING OF EVIL LAUGHTER AND PERFECT ACCENT ON "I VANT TO SUCK YOUR BLOOD." THE WORST WAS MARLYS WHO YELLED "YOU'RE CHEATING, YOU GUYS! I'M TELLING!" AS IF DRACULA EVER TALKED LIKE THAT.
YOU'RE SUPPOSED TO SAY "HAIL MARY 1-2-3" BEFORE YOU TOUCH THE BASE. YOU'RE OUT! AND QUIT MAKIN' THE SIGN OF THE CROSS AT ME, YA STUPE. IT'S TOO LATE. I SAID YOU ARE OUT! NOW GO TO MY COFFIN, I DON'T GOT ALL DAY.

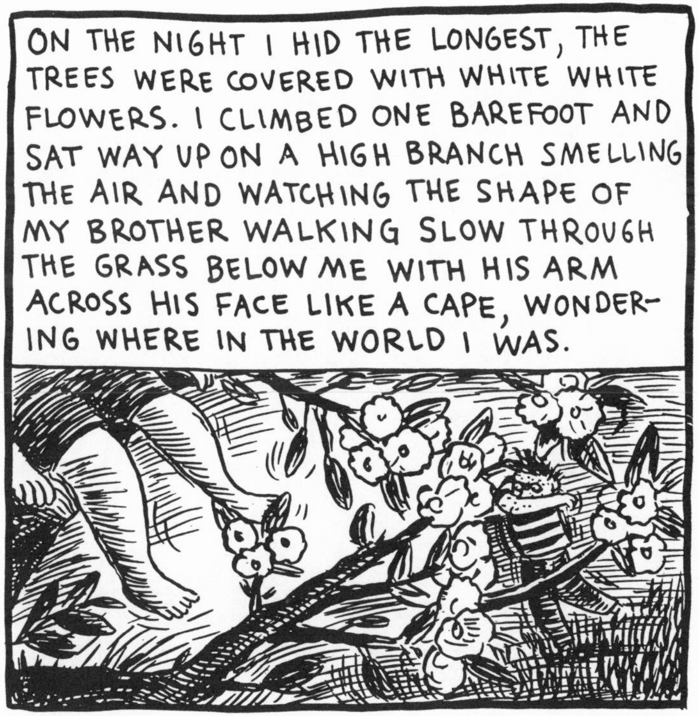
ON THE NIGHT I HID THE LONGEST, THE TREES WERE COVERED WITH WHITE WHITE FLOWERS. I CLIMBED ONE BAREFOOT AND SAT WAY UP ON A HIGH BRANCH SMELLING THE AIR AND WATCHING THE SHAPE OF MY BROTHER WALKING SLOW THROUGH THE GRASS BELOW ME WITH HIS ARM ACROSS HIS FACE LIKE A CAPE, WONDERING WHERE IN THE WORLD I WAS.

THE GOOD thING
BY LYNDA MORTIFIED BARRY © 1987
THIS ONE GUY, ROMEL, HAD A GRANDMA WHO LIVED BY HIS HOUSE AND THIS GRANDMA FRIED ROMEL BANANAS FOR BREAKFAST. I HAD NEVER SEEN NO FRIED BANANAS BEFORE. TO ROMEL IT WAS NORMAL.

SHE HAD BIG HOLES IN HER EARS WHICH I USED TO STARE AT WHEN THE THREE OF US PLAYED CARDS. AND SHE NEVER LET YOU WIN, NEITHER. ALSO SHE HARDLY NEVER WORE SHOES BUT IF SHE GOT MAD AT ROMEL, SHE'D CHASE HIM WITH A SLIPPER AND THROW IT AND ALWAYS HIT HIM RIGHT IN THE BUTT. HER AIM WAS SO GOOD SHE COULD HAVE BEEN ON T.V.
CRUISE MISSLE

BUT HER BEST THING OF ALL WAS HER WATCHING QUEEN FOR A DAY AND MAKING THE SIGN OF THE CROSS OVER AND OVER FOR THE CONTESTANTS. I AM NOT MAKING THIS UP BE-CAUSE NO ONE COULD MAKE THIS UP. ROMEL SAID DON'T SAY NOTHING TO HER ABOUT IT OR SHE'LL START ACTING NORMAL. WHAT AM I GONNA SAY ANYWAY TO A LADY WHO DOESN'T EVEN TALK ANY ENGLISH?
ARE YOU GONNA CUT THE CARDS OR ARE YOU GONNA KEEP STARIN' LIKE A RETARD?
MADRE DE DIOS!

ONE TIME ME AND ROMEL WENT IN ON SOME BUBBLE BATH AT THE PAY'N'SAVE TO GIVE HER AS A PRESENT. I DON'T EVEN THINK SHE KNEW WHAT IT WAS OR ANY-THING BUT SHE LIKED IT A LOT.

CAPS
LYNDA BARRY © 1988
WALK UP TO THE SCHOOL IN THE SUMMER AND YOU KNOW THAT GIRL THAT'S ALWAYS SITTING THERE ON THE TOP STEPS? WELL WATCH OUT FOR HER BECAUSE SHE SPITS. HER NAME IS TRACEY SOMETHING.

BY HER FEET THERES SO MUCH RED EXPLODED CAP PAPER AND AROUND A THOUSAND BURN MARKS ON THE CONCRETE. SHE POPS CAPS WITH ROCKS FOR THE SMELL. A GIRL LOVING THE SMELL OF CAPS.

SHE HAS A SCAR FROM HER LIP TO HER NOSE SO SHE DOESN'T LIKE ANYONE. I HAVE A COUSIN WITH THE SAME THING AND HE DOESN'T LIKE ANYONE EITHER BUT AT LEAST HE DOESN'T SPIT ON YOU TO PROVE IT.

SOMETIMES WHEN NO ONE'S AROUND, SHE UNPEELS A ROLL OF CAPS WITH HER FINGERNAIL AND THROWS IT DOWN TO ME. AND I POP THEM ALL FOR HER WHILE SHE WATCHES. EVERY ONE OF THOSE PERFECT BLACK BUMPS FOR HER.

MORNING STAR
BY LYNDA ONE TWO BARRY © 1987.
FOR A LITTLE WHILE, AFTER MY MOM GOT SICK, IT WAS THE NEIGHBOR LADY WHO TOOK US TO CHURCH. BUT WE DIDN'T GO TO OUR REGULAR CHURCH. WE WENT TO A DIFFERENT CHURCH THAT WAS INSIDE AN OLD STORE.
CHRISTMAS LIGHTS
PLASTIC FLOWERS
MICROPHONE
WALL AND FLOOR PAINTED BRIGHT BLUE
JESUS TAPED ONTO THE WALL
SPEAKER
PLASTIC FLOWERS
STYROFOAM CROSS WITH MAIL BOX LETTERS STUCK ON IT
CRACKS
PRAISE HIM

MY BROTHER LEANED OVER TO ME AND WHISPERED "WHAT KIND OF WACKY CHURCH IS THIS?" AND THEN A BEAUTIFUL LADY WITH BIG GIANT ARMS WALKS PAST US AND STARTS TO PLAY THE PIANO AND EVERYONE IS SINGING A SONG LIKE I HAVE NEVER HEARD BEFORE. I COULDN'T KEEP MY EYES OFF OF HER FOR EVEN ONE SINGLE SECOND.
I'M COMING UP ON THE ROUGH SIDE OF THE MOUNTAIN
I MUST HOLD TO GOD HIS POWERFUL HAND

PRETTY SOON THE GOD-MAN IS ASKING INTO THE MICROPHONE FOR OUR PRAYERS AND PEOPLE START TO STAND UP AND SHOUT AND SING AND CRY AND ME AND MY BROTHER, WE'VE NEVER SEEN ANYTHING LIKE IT, AND THAT LADY IS PLAYING THAT PIANO SO HARD I FEEL THE WORLD START TO SPIN AND SO DOES MY BROTHER BECAUSE HE TAKES MY HAND AND WE DON'T KNOW IF WE FEEL HORRIBLE OR WONDERFUL.

WHEN WE GET HOME I BEG MY BROTHER NOT TO TELL OUR MOM WHAT WE SAW. AND HOW AFTERWARDS PEOPLE STOOD OUT ON THE SIDEWALK LAUGHING AND SHAKING HANDS LIKE WHAT THEY JUST DID IN THERE WAS THE MOST NORMAL THING IN THE WORLD. MY MAMA WOULD SAY "THAT'S NO CHURCH!" BUT SEE, I WANT TO GO AGAIN.
WERE YOU COURTEOUS? DID YOU THANK MRS. GREEN?
YES MAMA

NEW NEIGHBORS
BY LYNDA BARRY ©1988
WHO MOVED IN NEXT DOOR WHERE NOBODY LASTED WAS THE DAWSINS. A MIXED UP COUPLE, BOTH OLD. MR. DAWSIN HAS A NAKED TATOO ON ONE ARM AND TAKES OUT HIS TEETH WHENEVER WE SAY HI. HE'S FRIENDLY.
MRS. DAWSIN IS FROM ANOTHER COUNTRY WHERE IT'S NORMAL TO SIT DOWN AND SMOKE A CIGARETTE WITH THE LIGHTED END IN YOUR MOUTH. HER MAIN ENGLISH TO US IS "NO MY DARLING" EVERYTIME WE BEG HER PLEASE PLEASE PLEASE TEACH US HER GREAT SMOKING ABILITY.

AND DON'T FORGET ABOUT THE CATS. 14, I SWEAR ON THE BIBLE. THEY BUILT A PEN ON THE BACK OF THE HOUSE AND I CAN SEE FROM MY BEDROOM THE CATS COMING OUT THE LITTLE DOOR, WALKING IN A CIRCLE AND GOING BACK IN NON STOP. MY AUNT SAYS MRS. DAWSIN'S PEOPLE EAT CATS BUT I COUNTED AND THERE'S STILL NONE MISSING.

I WAS OVER ENJOYING MR. DAWSIN SINGING TO HIS FAVORITE RECORD "COUNTING FLOWERS ON THE WALL" WITH HIS FACE ABOUT ONE INCH FROM THE SPEAKER, WHEN I NOTICED A LITTLE PICTURE OF A LADY, A HULA LADY, NEXT TO A SAILOR MAN. CAN YOU BELIEVE IT? IT'S THEM FROM ABOUT FIFTY THOUSAND YEARS AGO.

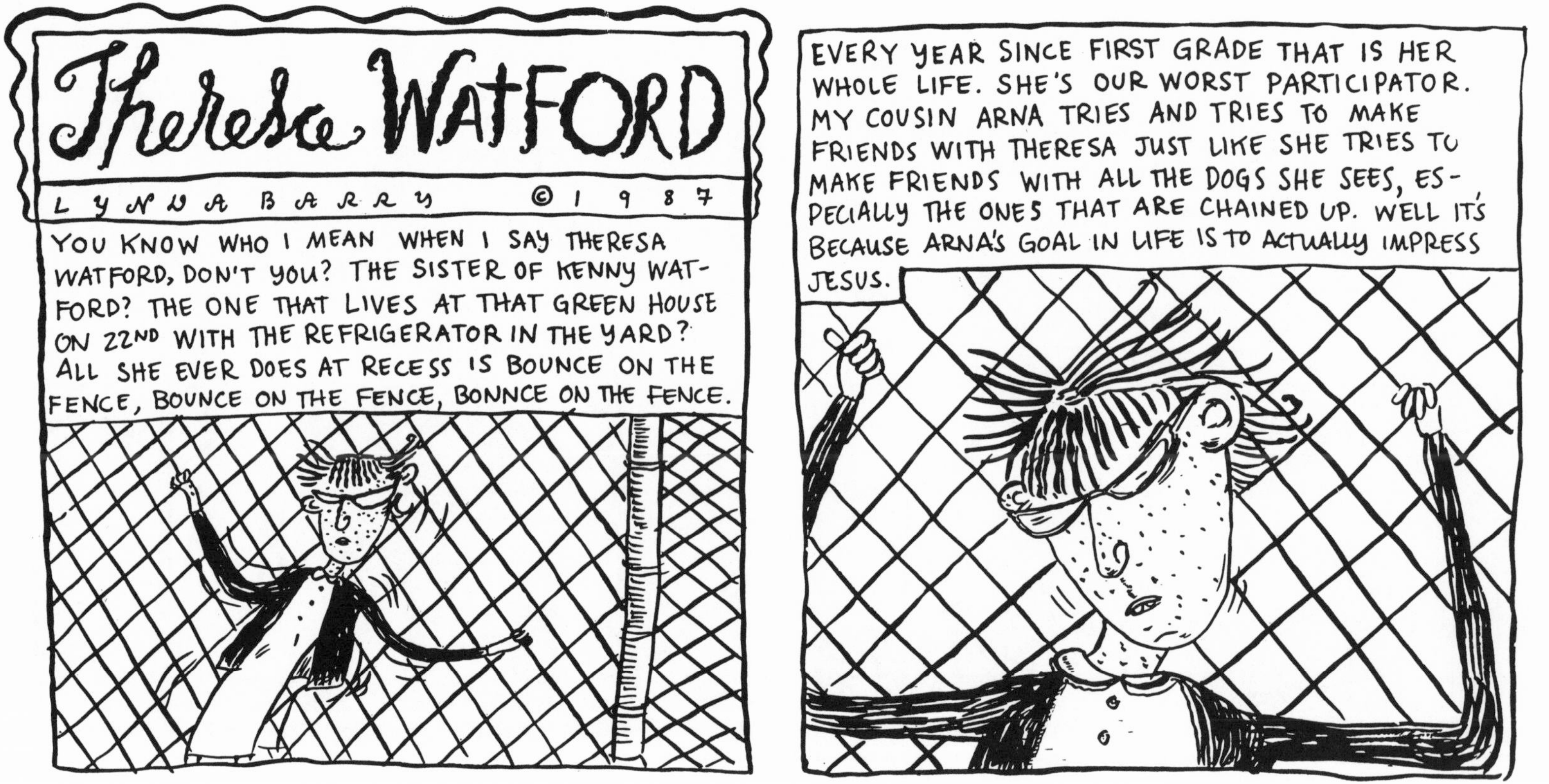
Theresa WATFORD
LYNDA BARRY ©1987
YOU KNOW WHO I MEAN WHEN I SAY THERESA WATFORD, DON'T YOU? THE SISTER OF KENNY WATFORD? THE ONE THAT LIVES AT THAT GREEN HOUSE ON 22ND WITH THE REFRIGERATOR IN THE YARD? ALL SHE EVER DOES AT RECESS IS BOUNCE ON THE FENCE, BOUNCE ON THE FENCE, BONNCE ON THE FENCE.
EVERY YEAR SINCE FIRST GRADE THAT IS HER WHOLE LIFE. SHE'S OUR WORST PARTICIPATOR. MY COUSIN ARNA TRIES AND TRIES TO MAKE FRIENDS WITH THERESA JUST LIKE SHE TRIES TO MAKE FRIENDS WITH ALL THE DOGS SHE SEES, ESPECIALLY THE ONES THAT ARE CHAINED UP. WELL IT'S BECAUSE ARNA'S GOAL IN LIFE IS TO ACTUALLY IMPRESS JESUS.

SO OK. IT'S FIRST RECESS, FIRST DAY OF SCHOOL AND THERE GOES THERESA TO THE FENCE AND BOUNCE BOUNCE BOUNCE, YOU KNOW, AND THERE GOES MY COUSIN ARNA WALKING VERY SLOW, THEN SHE'S TALKING TO THERESA, STANDING BACK FAR SO THE SPIT WON'T GET ON HER BECAUSE I FORGOT TO TELL YOU, THERESA SPITS. BUT THE ONLY ONE SHE EVER SPITS AT IS ARNA. IF SHE SPIT AT ME, I'D PUSH HER OVER, I'LL TELL YOU THAT MUCH.
HI THERESA WATFORD.
HI.
HI AND EVERYTHING.
HI.

AND LIKE EVERY YEAR, WE'RE STANDING THERE WITH THE BALL; ME, DIANE AND BARBARA, WAITING FOR THERESA TO HURRY UP AND SPIT SO THAT ARNA CAN GIVE UP AND COME BACK AND PLAY FOUR SQUARE, BUT THIS YEAR THERESA WATFORD WON'T SPIT. SHE WON'T. AND IF SHE DOESN'T SPIT, ARNA'S GOING TO GET STUCK BEING HER FRIEND AND SHE'LL BE RUINED. AND I'M RUINED BECAUSE I'M HER COUSIN AND THEN DIANE AND BARBARA-- SPIT, THERESA! SPIT OR I SWEAR TO GOD I'LL CREAM YOU!!
HI.

WHO'S HE?
L·Y·N·D·A·B·A·R·R·Y © ·1·9·8·8·0·
YOU KNOW THAT NEW KID DEWEY WHOSE REAL NAME IS SOMETHING-SOMETHING IN SPANISH? WHOSE FATHER HAS THAT MUSTACHE AND YOU CAN'T TELL IF HE'S A MEXICAN, A NEGRO, OR WHAT?
SAY YOUR NAME AGAIN.
DEWEY.
I'M MARLYS. M-A-R-L-Y-S. O.K. WHAT'S MY NAME?

HE HAS A BEAUTY MARK ON HIS FOREHEAD AND A STEEL TOOTH AND HE CAN DO THE SPLITS LIKE HIS FAVORITE HERO OF A SINGER, JAMES BROWN. OUR MOM SAYS HE'S GOING TO WRECK HIS PANTS.
I'VE GOT SOUL
AN' I'M SUPERBAD
UGH!

HE TOLD US JESUS CAME INTO HIS BEDROOM ONE NIGHT AND HE WAS WEARING A HAIR NET. HE SAID JESUS FLOATED ABOVE HIS BED AND TOLD HIM TO PLEASE BUILD HIM SOMETHING NICE OUT OF POPSICLE STICKS.

WHAT HE DECIDED TO BUILD JESUS WAS A GO-CART. MY BROTHER ARNOLD SAID "THERE'S NO WAY JESUS WOULD RIDE A GO-CART. OBVIOUSLY MAKE HIM A CROSS."
BUT IN DEWEY'S OPINION, JESUS WOULD BE HAPPIER ON A GO-CART.
STYLE ME THE GLUE BOTTLE, MAN.
HUH?
GIMME THE GLUE.
ELMO'S GLUE

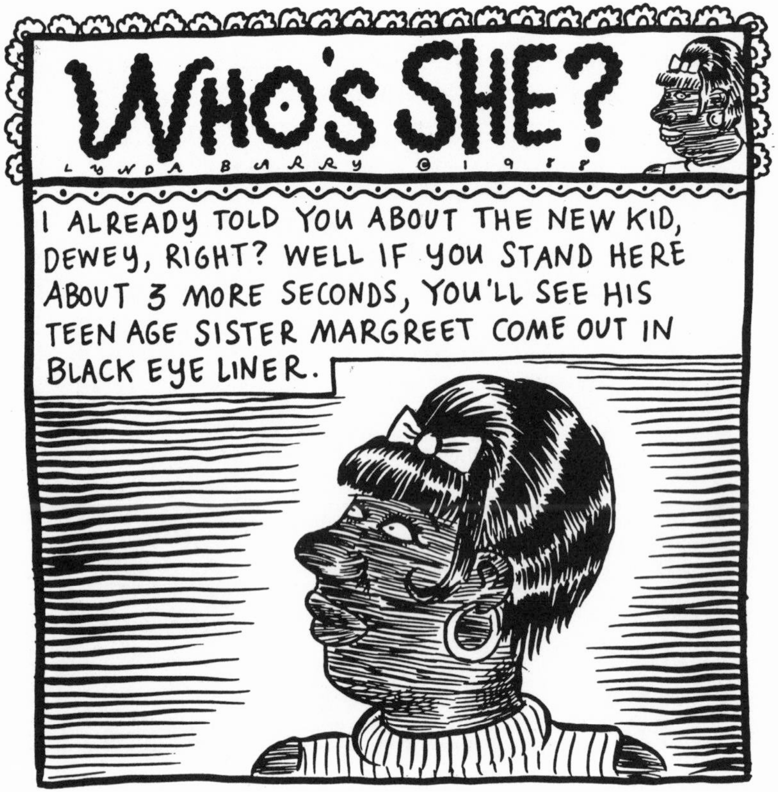

WHO'S SHE?
LYNDA BARRY ©1988
I ALREADY TOLD YOU ABOUT THE NEW KID, DEWEY, RIGHT? WELL IF YOU STAND HERE ABOUT 3 MORE SECONDS, YOU'LL SEE HIS TEEN AGE SISTER MARGREET COME OUT IN BLACK EYE LINER.

SHE WRITES HER MOTTO OF B.S.S. ON EVERYTHING. IT GOES FOR "BOLD SOUL SISTER." SHE LISTENS TO KYAC SOUL RADIO AND LAST NIGHT WHEN THE SONG "SOUL FINGER" CAME ON, SHE DID A SOUL TRAIN ON TOP OF THEIR STATION WAGON UNTIL HER MOTHER CAME OUT AND TOLD HER TO KNOCK IT OFF IN SPANISH.

MY COUSIN MAYBONNE WHO'S IN HER SAME GRADE, AT FIRST THOUGHT SHE WAS STUCK-UP BECAUSE OF HER GREAT CLOTHES. MAYBONNE SAID "JUST BECAUSE SOMEONE HAS LACE-UP HIP HUGGERS DOES NOT MEAN THEY CAN CONTROL THE WORLD." THEN MAGREET LET HER WEAR THOSE PANTS. WHEN MY AUNT SAW THEM ON HER SHE SHOUTED "ARE YOU TRYING TO KILL ME?!"
I SAID COLD, BOLD, AND TOGETHER, BAY-BAY

NOW THEY'RE BEST FRIENDS EXCEPT AT SCHOOL BECAUSE NO B.S.S. CAN SIT WITH A WHITE HONKEY BITCH AT THEIR LUNCHROOM. SAME GOES FOR W.H.B.'s TO B.S.S.'s ONLY BACKWARDS. BUT MAYBONNE SAYS THEY HAVE A SECRET SIGN THAT THEY WON'T REVEAL TO NO ONE NOT EVEN FOR $5.00.

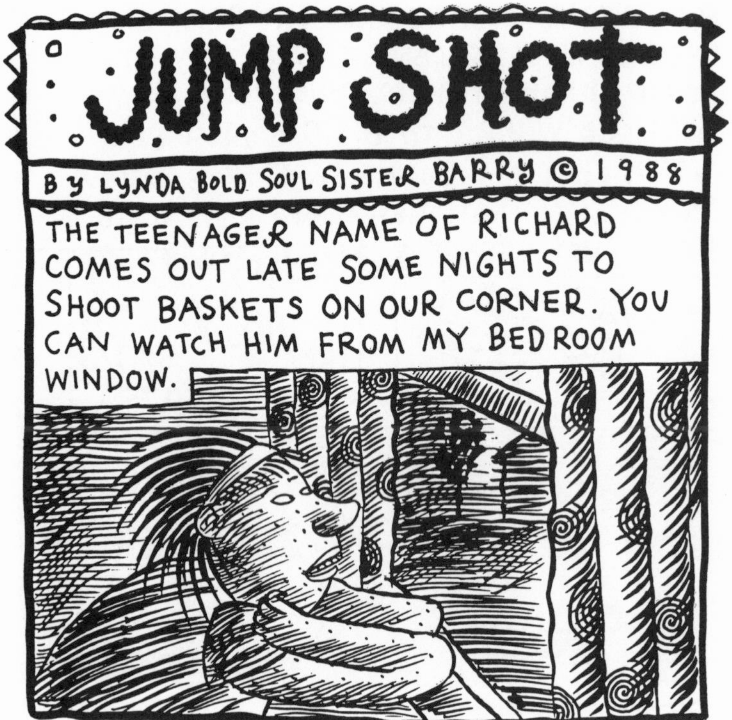
JUMP SHOT
BY LYNDA BOLD SOUL SISTER BARRY © 1988
THE TEENAGER NAME OF RICHARD COMES OUT LATE SOME NIGHTS TO SHOOT BASKETS ON OUR CORNER. YOU CAN WATCH HIM FROM MY BEDROOM WINDOW.

YOU CAN LAY ON THE BED AND HEAR THE BALL, THE PING PING OF IT AGAINST THE STREET BOUNCING. YOU CAN HEAR HIM WALK IT, THEN RUN IT AND DO HIS PERFECT HOOK SHOT.

BOUNCE, BOUNCE, BOUNCE, STOP. THE FAST NO-SOUND OF HIS FEET IN THE AIR, THE BALL FLYING UP, PAUSE, THEN WHAM-WHAM AGAINST THE BACK BOARD, A HIGH BOUNCE OFF THE RIM, HIM WHISPERING SON OF A BITCH.

HIM JUMPING UP ON THE CORNER, HIM JUMPING HIGH AND TURNING IN THE AIR UNDER A STREET LIGHT WITH A THOUSAND MILLION BUGS FLYING AROUND IT GOING WILD, WILD, WILD.

MOVING AWAY
BY LYNDA SLAMMER DOOR BARRY © 1987
UP THE STREET, ON THE DIRT PART OF THE ROAD, WAS THE HOUSE OF LOUIS CHEEK AND HIS SISTER SANDRA CHEEK. NONE OF US EVER LIKED THEM BECAUSE THEY HAD BAD TEMPERS, SO "BIG DEAL" IS ALL WE THOUGHT WHEN LOUIS TOLD US THEY WERE MOVING AWAY.
AND YOU GUYS WANNA KNOW WHERE WE'RE MOVIN' TO?
HUH?
WE'RE MOVIN' OVER TO DISNEY-LAND.
I'M GONNA LIVE AT DISNEYLAND YOU GUYS.
HOW COME PAPER ALWAYS STICKS TO POPSICLES?

LOUIS YELLED AT US THAT WE WOULD NEVER EVER SEE HIM AGAIN FOR THE REST OF OUR LIVES. HE WAS STANDING ON HIS PORCH WHEN HE YELLED IT AND HE YELLED IT ABOUT NINE HUNDRED THOUSAND TIMES 'TIL HIS MOM'S ARM CAME OUT THE DOOR AND YANKED HIM INSIDE. WE WERE TOTALLY USED TO LOUIS'S YELLING ANYWAY.
WHO EVEN CARES 'CAUSE I HATE ALL YOUR GUTSES ANYWAY!
THE END!
YOU'LL BE SORRY!
I HATE YOU. I'M GLAD I'LL NEVER SEE YOU GUYS AGAIN!
SHOVE OVER ARNA. WHAT A HOG.
K'MON ARNA MAN! YOUR TURN.
DANG.
ARE YOU PLAYING?

I WANT TO TELL YOU THAT NONE OF US EVEN KNEW WHAT MOVING AWAY WAS UNTIL WE ALL WALKED OVER TO LOUIS'S HOUSE AND SEEN IT WAS TOTALLY EMPTY. MY BROTHER AND MARLYS BOOSTED ME UP THROUGH THE WINDOW SO I COULD GO INSIDE AND OPEN THE DOOR. MAINLY I NOTICED A SMELL. THE SMELL OF LOUIS AND HIS SISTER. AND SEEING STUFF ON THE FLOOR, LIKE A BLUE CURLER AND SOME MATCHES. IT GAVE ME THE SHIVERS.

AND EVEN THOUGH WE NEVER LIKED LOUIS WE DIDN'T THINK IT WAS ANY FAIR THAT WE WOULD NEVER, FOR THE REST OF OUR WHOLE ENTIRE LIVES, GET TO SEE HIM AGAIN. MY BROTHER MADE US A BET WE WOULD SEE HIM SOMEWHERE IF WE KEPT LOOKING AROUND BUT YOU KNOW WE NEVER DID.
AND EVEN THOUGH A BUNCH OF DIFFERENT FAMILIES LIVED IN THAT HOUSE LATER ON WE STILL CALLED IT LOUIS CHEEK'S HOUSE. THAT WAS THE REAL NAME OF IT AND SINCE WE WERE THERE THE LONGEST, WE MADE THE RULES.
YOU'RE THE ONE WHO LIVES OVER AT LOUIS CHEEK'S HOUSE NOW, RIGHT?
IT AIN'T NO LOUIS CHEEK'S HOUSE, SO QUIT CALLIN' IT THAT. IT'S MY DAD'S HOUSE.

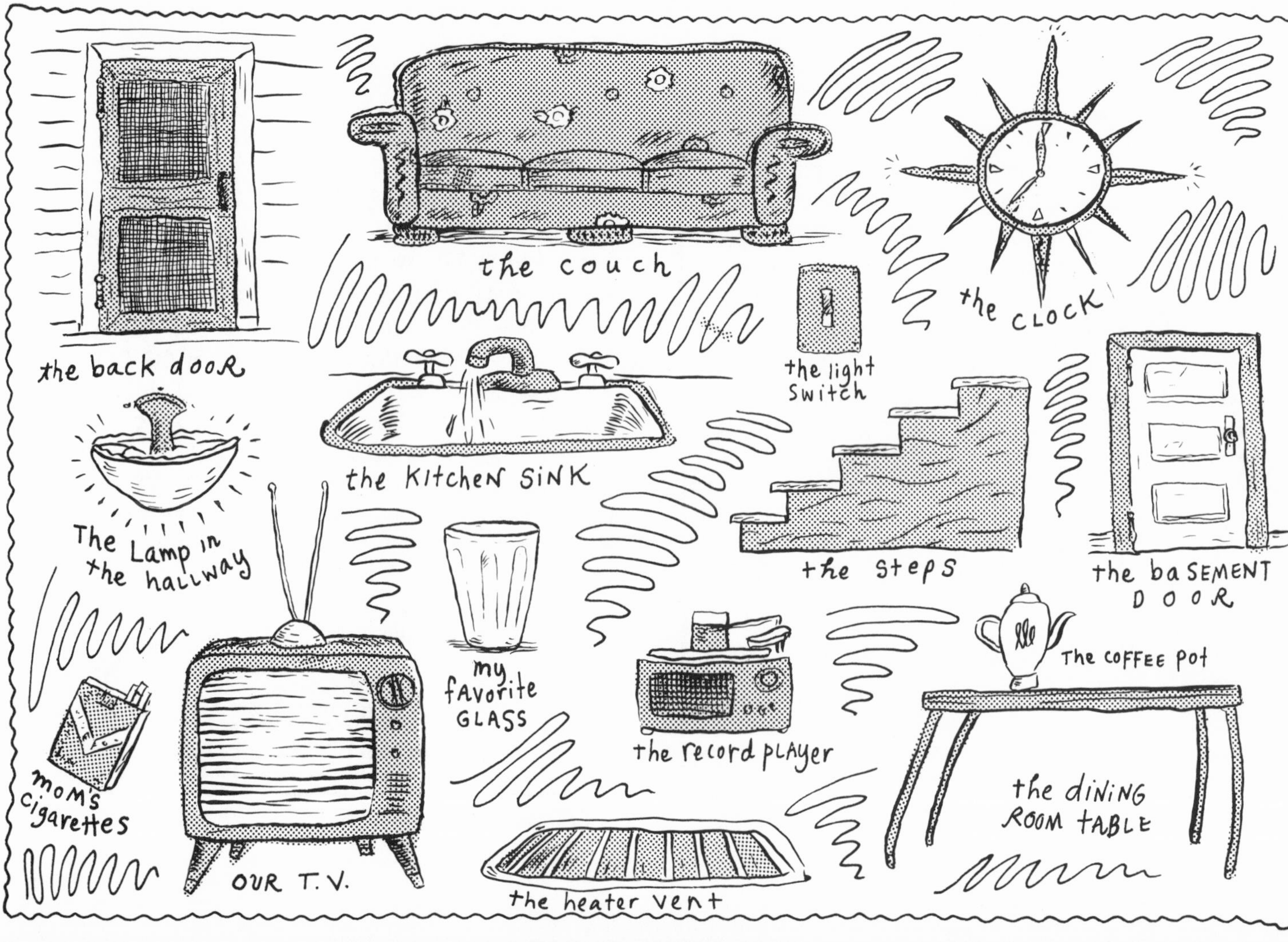
the back door
the couch
the CLOCK
the light switch
the kitchen SINK
The Lamp in the hallway
the steps
the basement DOOR
my favorite GLASS
the coffee pot
the record player
mom's cigarettes
OUR T.V.
the dining ROOM table
the heater vent

HOME AND FAMILY

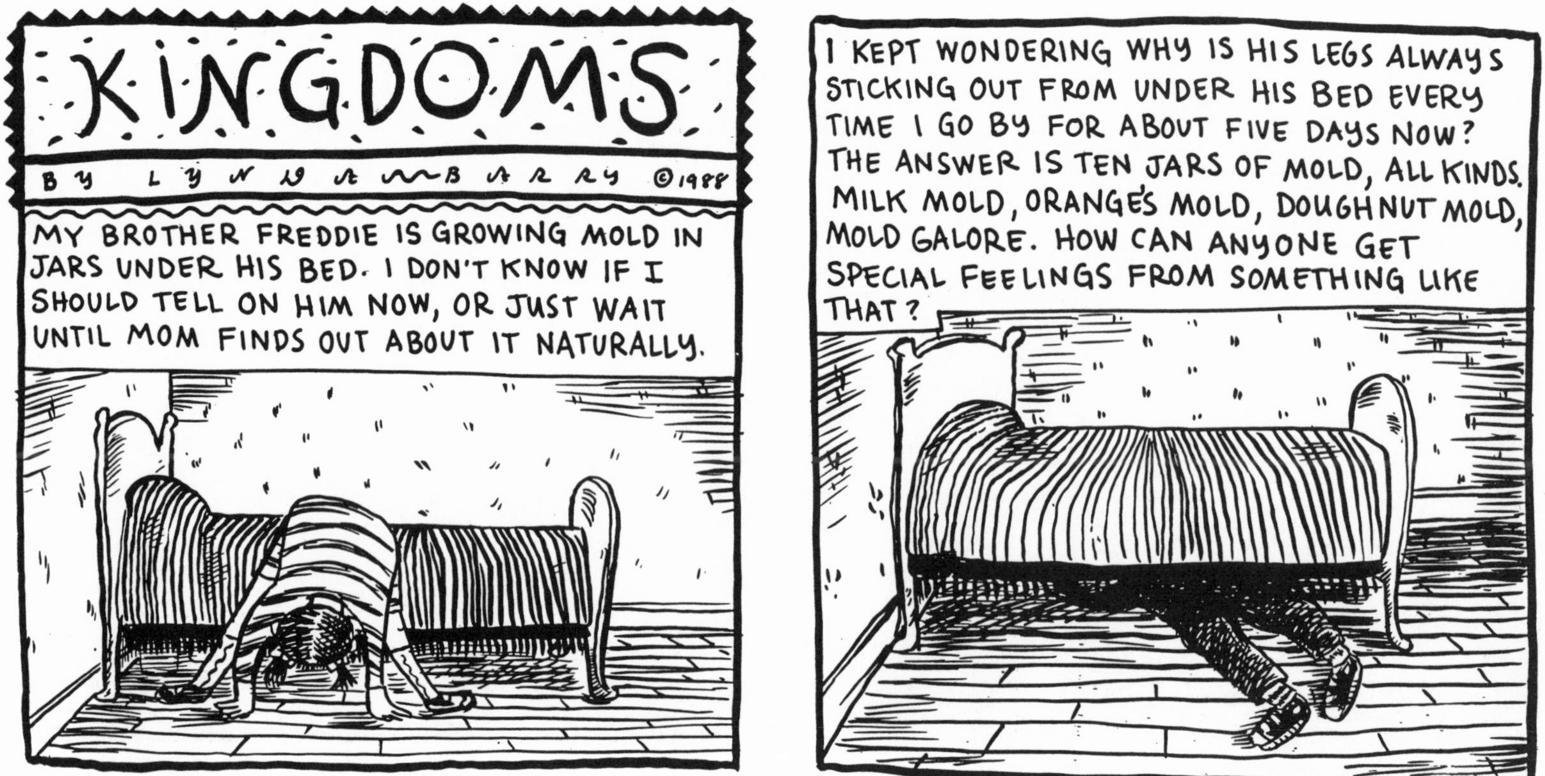
KINGDOMS
BY LYNDA BARRY ©1988
MY BROTHER FREDDIE IS GROWING MOLD IN JARS UNDER HIS BED. I DON'T KNOW IF I SHOULD TELL ON HIM NOW, OR JUST WAIT UNTIL MOM FINDS OUT ABOUT IT NATURALLY.
I KEPT WONDERING WHY IS HIS LEGS ALWAYS STICKING OUT FROM UNDER HIS BED EVERY TIME I GO BY FOR ABOUT FIVE DAYS NOW? THE ANSWER IS TEN JARS OF MOLD, ALL KINDS. MILK MOLD, ORANGE'S MOLD, DOUGHNUT MOLD, MOLD GALORE. HOW CAN ANYONE GET SPECIAL FEELINGS FROM SOMETHING LIKE THAT?

LAST NIGHT I SAW HIM SNEAK THE FLASH-LIGHT UP FROM THE BASEMENT AND I SAID "I'M TELLING" AND HE SAID "OK BUT COME LOOK FIRST." WE LAID ON OUR STOMACHS UNDER HIS BED AS HE FEATURED EACH ONE OF THE MOLDS IN THE SPOTLIGHT. HE TOLD ME THERE WAS A WHOLE MIDGET KINGDOM IN EVERY ONE OF HIS JARS.

HE TOLD ME A POLICEMAN CUT HIS FACE SHAVING ONE MORNING AND HIS WIFE PUT SOME MOLDY BREAD ON IT AND HE GOT INSTANTLY HEALED. "WHAT A DISCOVERY!" MY BROTHER SAID.
SO THATS WHY I GOT THIS CORN IN THE BABY FOOD JAR SAVED FROM LUNCH TO GIVE TO HIM AS A SURPRISE. SOME TIMES IT JUST KILLS ME THE THINGS HE DOES.
YOO HOO
FREDDIE..

FREDDIE
BY LYNDA BARRY ©1987
MY COUSIN MARLYS'S LITTLE BROTHER WAS NAMED MY COUSIN FREDDIE WHO WAS WAY YOUNGER THAN US BY TWO WHOLE YEARS. MARLYS SAID HER MOM SAID FREDDIE WAS AN ACCIDENT. LIKE WHEN YOU DROP YOUR GLASS OF MILK AND IT BREAKS AND SPILLS.
NONE OF US WAS AN ACCIDENT. ONLY FREDDIE. PERSONALLY, I THINK IT MADE HIM A LOT DIFFERENT FROM US. ALSO, I THINK IF A FAIRY TALE WAS EVER GOING TO HAPPEN IN REAL LIFE, WHO IT WOULD HAPPEN TO WAS SECRETLY FREDDIE. JUST LOOK AT THE FACTS: HE COULDN'T EVEN STAND TO STEP ON A BEE. SOMETIMES IT WOULD MAKE YOU WANT TO SLUG HIM. AND SOMETIMES YOU DID.
CHICKEN. WHAT A CHICKEN.
BUT WHAT IF IT'S THE MAMA BEE? AND THEN SHE'S DEAD AND ALL THE BABY BEES GET LEFT ALONE LIKE ON THE WONDERFUL WORLD OF DISNEY?
THERE AIN'T NO DISNEY MOVIE ABOUT BEES, MAN.

HE WAS SO GOOD THAT USUALLY WE HAD TO DITCH HIM IN ORDER TO EVEN PLAY RIGHT. IT'S NOT LIKE HE WOULD TELL ON YOU. IT'S THAT HE WOULD FEEL SO BAD IF HE WAS EVEN JUST WITH US WHEN WE DID SOMETHING AGAINST THE RULES, THAT IT WOULD MAINLY JUST WRECK EVERYTHING FOR EVERYBODY. MOSTLY WE DID NOT WANT HIM AROUND US. WHO WOULD EVER? HIS MOM WOULD ALWAYS LAUGH AND SAY "HOW DID YOU TURN OUT THIS WAY? I DON'T THINK YOU'RE REALLY MY SON."
CAN I HELP YOU DO SOME STUFF, MOM?
NOT NOW FREDDIE. WHY DON'T YOU GO OUTSIDE AND PLAY WITH THE OTHER KIDS. YOU STAY INSIDE TOO MUCH.
O.K.

WE PROBABLY WOULDN'T PICK ON HIM ALL OF THE TIME IF HE COULD JUST DO SOMETHING NORMAL LIKE THROW ROCKS AT THE SCHOOL, BUT HE CAN'T. I GUESS MAYBE IT'S BECAUSE WHEN YOU'RE ALREADY AN ACCIDENT, YOU CAN'T AFFORD TO MESS UP AGAIN.

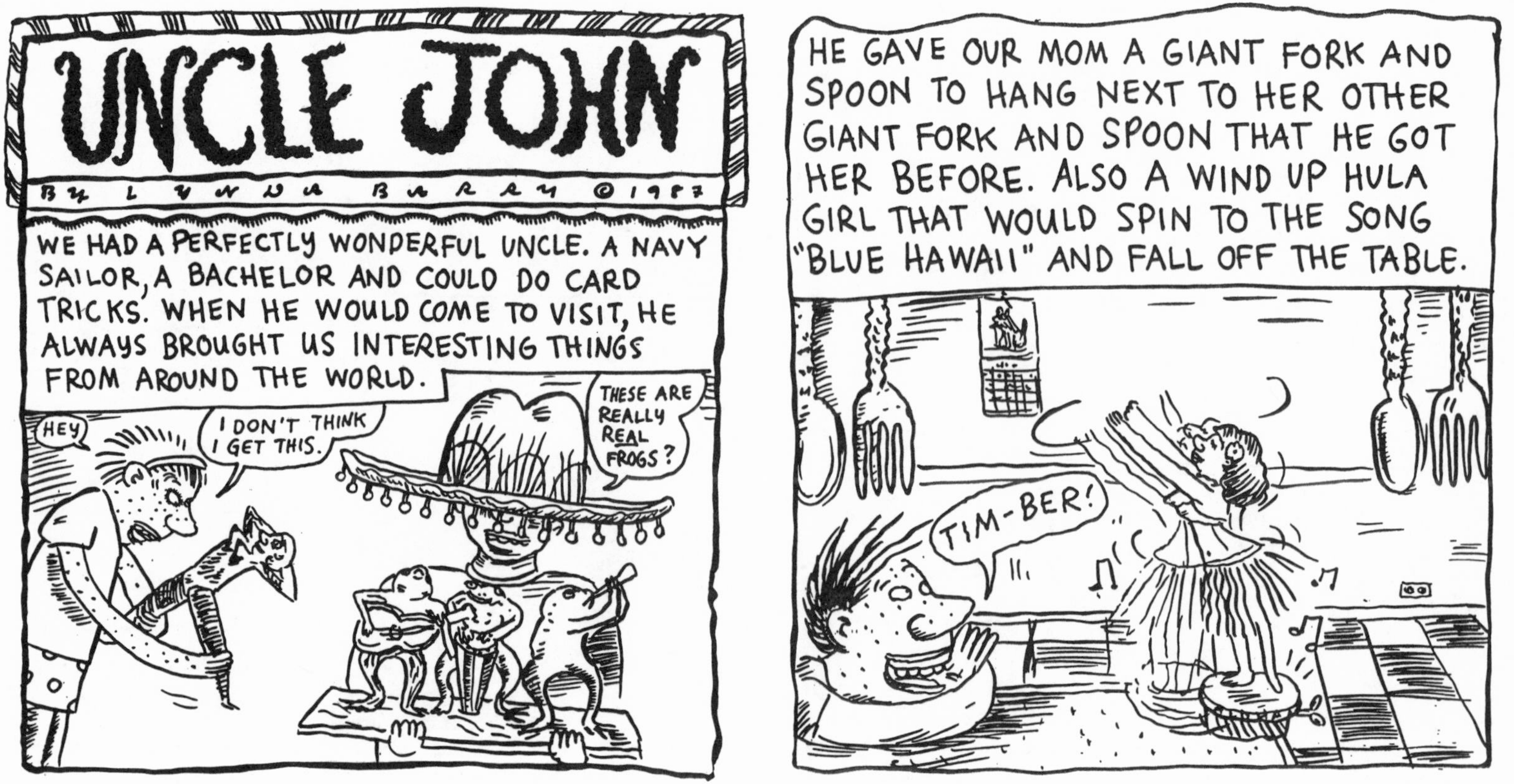
UNCLE JOHN
BY LYNDA BARRY ©1987
WE HAD A PERFECTLY WONDERFUL UNCLE. A NAVY SAILOR, A BACHELOR AND COULD DO CARD TRICKS. WHEN HE WOULD COME TO VISIT, HE ALWAYS BROUGHT US INTERESTING THINGS FROM AROUND THE WORLD.
HEY
I DON'T THINK I GET THIS.
THESE ARE REALLY REAL FROGS?
HE GAVE OUR MOM A GIANT FORK AND SPOON TO HANG NEXT TO HER OTHER GIANT FORK AND SPOON THAT HE GOT HER BEFORE. ALSO A WIND UP HULA GIRL THAT WOULD SPIN TO THE SONG "BLUE HAWAII" AND FALL OFF THE TABLE.
TIM-BER!

MY SISTER GOT THIS STRAW HAT WITH FAKE HAIR SEWED TO IT WHICH SHE THOUGHT CAUSED HER TO BE A FASHION MODEL AND SHE WORE IT CONSTANTLY UNTIL IT GOT CAUGHT IN THE FAN ABOUT 10 MINUTES AFTER UNCLE JOHN GAVE IT TO HER.
DOES SHE OR DOESN'T SHE?
ONLY HER HAIRDRESSER KNOWS FOR SURE.

BEFORE UNCLE JOHN LEFT AGAIN HE GAVE ME A DECK OF NAKED LADY CARDS WHICH MY FRIEND'S MOM GOT SO MAD ABOUT ME BRINGING INTO THEIR HOUSE THAT SHE MADE ME MARCH RIGHT INTO THE BATHROOM AND FLUSH THEM DOWN THE TOILET WHERE THEY BELONG AND THEN THERE WAS THIS SUCKING NOISE AND ALL THE CARDS AND WATER CAME UP AND THEY HAD TO CALL A PLUMBER.
UNCLE JOHN IF YOU ARE READING THIS, WE MISS YOU.
HELLO?
YES, THIS IS ARNOLD'S MOTHER...
WELL HELLO MRS. BUCKHOLT, WHAT CAN I DO FOR YOU?
HE WHAT?!

THIS STORY
LYNDA • BARRY • © 1987
IT WAS MY SISTER ARNA WHO FOUND HIM AND SHE LET OUT SUCH A CRY AND A SCREAM THAT OUR MOM CAME RUNNING IN AND SLAPPED HER FOR SCARING US SO BAD. THEN MOM SAW MICKEY. YOU NEVER KNEW MICKEY, DID YOU, OUR DOG?

MOM SAID OH JESUS. GET YOUR COATS, KIDS. GET A BOX. THERE WAS BLOOD ALL OVER. OH LORD, SHE SAYS. GET SOME NEWSPAPER.

IN THE BACK SEAT WE SHARE THE TIDE BOX ON OUR KNEES. ARNA KEEPS SAYING MICKEY MICKEY BOY HERE MICKEY AND HE'S STILL BREATHING BUT HE CAN'T TURN HIS EYES TO US. YOU KNOW HOW THE WHOLE WORLD JUST STARTS TO FEEL LIKE ITS FLOATING?

THEN WE'RE AT THE DOG POUND. TO PUT HIM OUT OF HIS MISERY, OUR MOM SAYS. YOU WAIT, SHE SAYS. SHE GOES INSIDE TO GET A MAN. AND WE SIT THERE JUST SITTING THERE LIKE WE'RE FROZEN, FEELING MICKEY WARM THROUGH THE BOX ON OUR LEGS.

SWEAR KING
STORY BY JOHN MULLEN · TOLD BY LYNDA BARRY © 1988
MY COUSIN FREDDIE HAS A SECRET IDENTITY. IT HAPPENED BY ACCIDENT. HE IS THE SWEAR KING. SOMETHING HE NEVER WANTED TO BE IN THE FIRST PLACE.

IT STARTED WHEN HE WENT UP PAST 23rd TO FIND OUT ABOUT THE LIFE OF INSECTS ON OTHER STREETS AND THESE BOYS CAUGHT HIM AND TOLD HIM TO SAY THE WORD SON OF A BITCH. FREDDIE TOLD THEM THAT WAS NOTHING AND STARTED SAYING SUCH CRAZY SWEARS I GUESS HE ACTUALLY GOT FAMOUS UP THERE.

TODAY, ONE OF THEIR MOMS DRIVES UP WITH FREDDIE IN HER CAR AND WE COULD TELL BY HIS FACE AND THE WAY SHE CAME UP THE STEPS THAT HE WAS IN BIG TROUBLE. SO THAT'S WHY HE'S GROUNDED AND THAT'S WHY HE KEEPS STARING OUT THE WINDOWS AT THOSE MILLION JARS OF BUGS PILED UP IN THE OUTSIDE GARBAGE CANS.

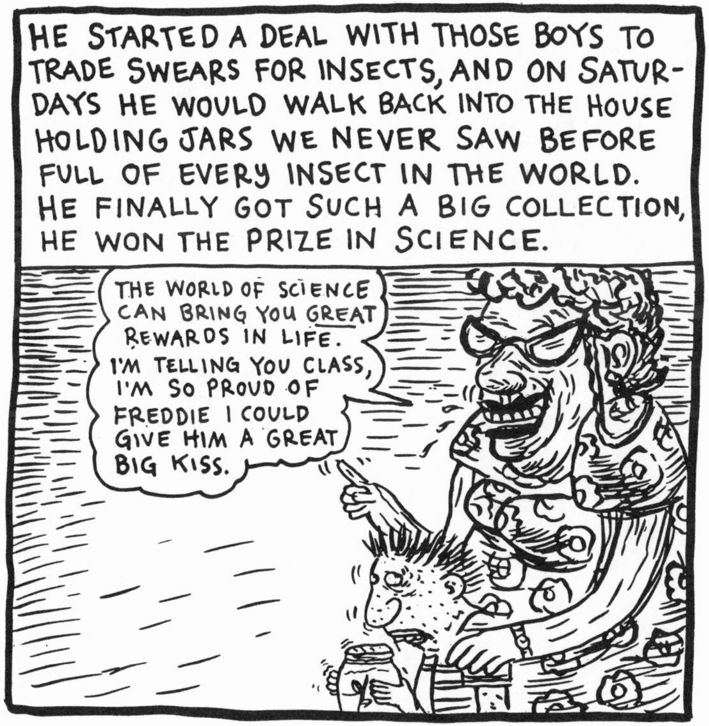
HE STARTED A DEAL WITH THOSE BOYS TO TRADE SWEARS FOR INSECTS, AND ON SATURDAYS HE WOULD WALK BACK INTO THE HOUSE HOLDING JARS WE NEVER SAW BEFORE FULL OF EVERY INSECT IN THE WORLD. HE FINALLY GOT SUCH A BIG COLLECTION, HE WON THE PRIZE IN SCIENCE.
THE WORLD OF SCIENCE CAN BRING YOU GREAT REWARDS IN LIFE. I'M TELLING YOU CLASS, I'M SO PROUD OF FREDDIE I COULD GIVE HIM A GREAT BIG KISS.

RED COMB
L Y N D A B A R R Y ©88
EVERYBODY KNOWS A BAD INFLUENCE. ON OUR STREET IT WAS KENNY WATFORD WHO COULD WHISTLE SO LOUD. HE ALWAYS SAID TO YOU "MEET ME IN THE WOODS, MEET ME IN THE WOODS" AND SOMETIMES YOU DID.

HE WAS SO HANDSOME WITH A TAN SCAR DOWN HIS CHEEK AND BLACK BLACK HAIR HE WOULD ASK YOU TO COMB. HIM SITTING ALONE ON SOME CARDBOARD IN THE RAVINE, HOLDING OUT THE RED COMB TO YOU JUST TEN STEPS AWAY.

AND HE WOULD SAY IT. "I WANT TO BE YOUR BOYFRIEND, SECRETLY I AM YOUR BOYFRIEND, HONEY." AND YOU WOULD STAND THERE PRETENDING SOMETHING ELSE WAS HAPPENING, ANYTHING ELSE.

AND LATER, WAY LATER, WHEN YOU HEAR HIS WHISTLE SCREAMING FROM THE CORNER, YOU'LL TURN UP THE KNOB ON THE TV SO LOUD THAT YOUR MOTHER WILL FINALLY COME RUNNING IN AND STOP YOU.

AUNT LESLIE
LYNDA BARRY © 1988
BOTH ME AND MARLYS HAVE A GORGEOUS AUNT, AUNT LESLIE WHO'S NOT MARRIED, WHO HAS ALL GOLD FILLINGS, WHO COMES TO VISIT. SHE WEARS BEAUTIFUL EYE LINER.

SHE HAS SUCH LONG HAIR THAT WE DIVIDE IN HALF AND COMB WHILE SHE CLOSES HER EYES AND TELLS REAL STORIES OF VAMPIRES LIVING IN HOTELS WHERE THE CEILINGS DRIP BLOOD. SHE LETS ARNOLD AND FREDDIE RUB HER NYLONS.

SHE LETS HER HAIR DRY BY LAYING THE WRONG WAY ON MY BED, BARE FOOT, READING OFF LIMITS LOVE MAGAZINES AND SMOKING FILTER TIPS. I ADORE THE SMELL OF SMOKE IN MY ROOM.

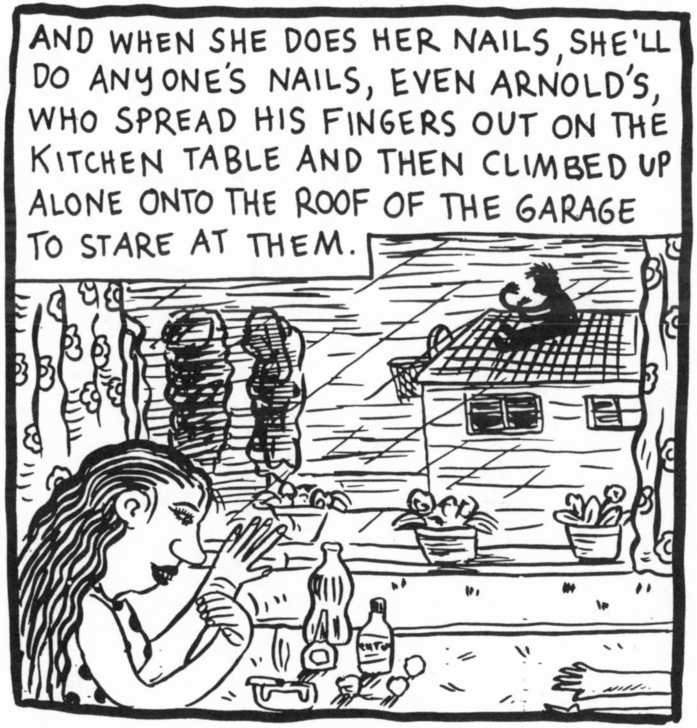
AND WHEN SHE DOES HER NAILS, SHE'LL DO ANYONE'S NAILS, EVEN ARNOLD'S, WHO SPREAD HIS FINGERS OUT ON THE KITCHEN TABLE AND THEN CLIMBED UP ALONE ONTO THE ROOF OF THE GARAGE TO STARE AT THEM.

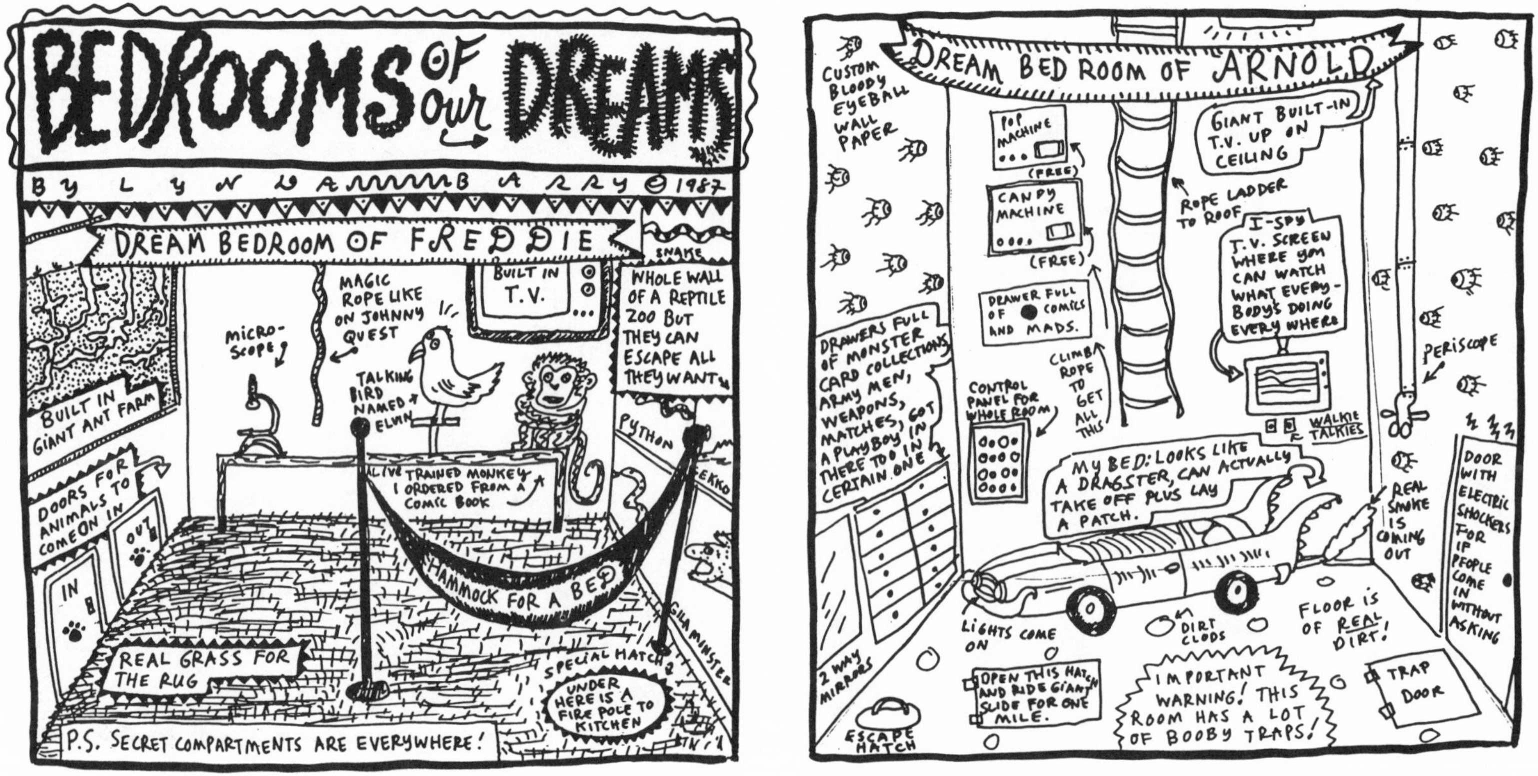
BEDROOMS OF OUR DREAMS
BY LYNDA BARRY © 1987
DREAM BEDROOM OF FREDDIE
MAGIC ROPE LIKE ON JOHNNY QUEST
BUILT IN T.V.
WHOLE WALL OF A REPTILE ZOO BUT THEY CAN ESCAPE ALL THEY WANT
SNAKE
MICRO-SCOPE
TALKING BIRD NAMED ELVIN
BUILT IN GIANT ANT FARM
PYTHON
GEKKO
ALIVE TRAINED MONKEY I ORDERED FROM A COMIC BOOK
DOORS FOR ANIMALS TO COME ON IN
OUT
IN
HAMMOCK FOR A BED
GILA MONSTER
REAL GRASS FOR THE RUG
SPECIAL HATCH
UNDER HERE IS A FIRE POLE TO KITCHEN
P.S. SECRET COMPARTMENTS ARE EVERYWHERE!
DREAM BED ROOM OF ARNOLD
CUSTOM BLOODY EYEBALL WALL PAPER
POP MACHINE
(FREE)
CANDY MACHINE
(FREE)
GIANT BUILT-IN T.V. UP ON CEILING
ROPE LADDER TO ROOF
DRAWER FULL OF COMICS AND MADS.
I-SPY T.V. SCREEN WHERE YOU CAN WATCH WHAT EVERYBODY'S DOING EVERY WHERE
DRAWERS FULL OF MONSTER CARD COLLECTIONS ARMY MEN, WEAPONS, MATCHES, GOT A PLAYBOY IN THERE TOO IN CERTAIN ONE
CLIMB A ROPE TO GET ALL THIS
CONTROL PANEL FOR WHOLE ROOM
PERISCOPE
WALKIE TALKIES
MY BED: LOOKS LIKE A DRAGSTER, CAN ACTUALLY TAKE OFF PLUS LAY A PATCH.
REAL SNAKE IS COMING OUT
DOOR WITH ELECTRIC SHOCKERS FOR IF PEOPLE COME IN WITHOUT ASKING
LIGHTS COME ON
DIRT CLODS
FLOOR IS OF REAL DIRT!
2 WAY MIRRORS
OPEN THIS HATCH AND RIDE GIANT SLIDE FOR ONE MILE.
IMPORTANT WARNING! THIS ROOM HAS A LOT OF BOOBY TRAPS!
TRAP DOOR
ESCAPE HATCH

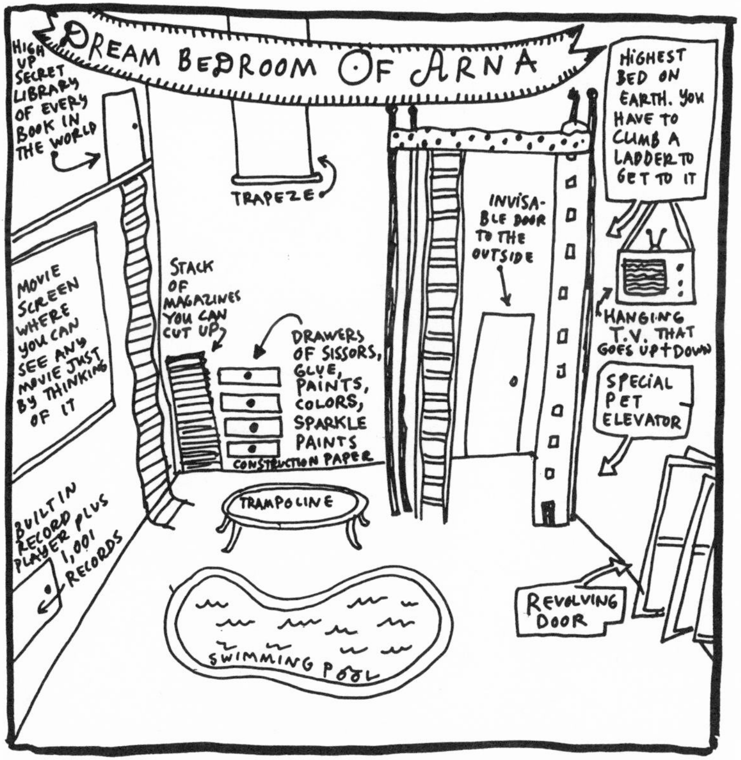
DREAM BEDROOM OF ARNA
HIGH UP SECRET LIBRARY OF EVERY BOOK IN THE WORLD
TRAPEZE
HIGHEST BED ON EARTH. YOU HAVE TO CLIMB A LADDER TO GET TO IT
INVISABLE DOOR TO THE OUTSIDE
MOVIE SCREEN WHERE YOU CAN SEE ANY MOVIE JUST BY THINKING OF IT
STACK OF MAGAZINES YOU CAN CUT UP
DRAWERS OF SISSORS, GLUE, PAINTS, COLORS, SPARKLE PAINTS
CONSTRUCTION PAPER
HANGING T.V. THAT GOES UP+DOWN
SPECIAL PET ELEVATOR
TRAMPOLINE
BUILTIN RECORD PLAYER PLUS 1,001 RECORDS
REVOLVING DOOR
SWIMMING POOL

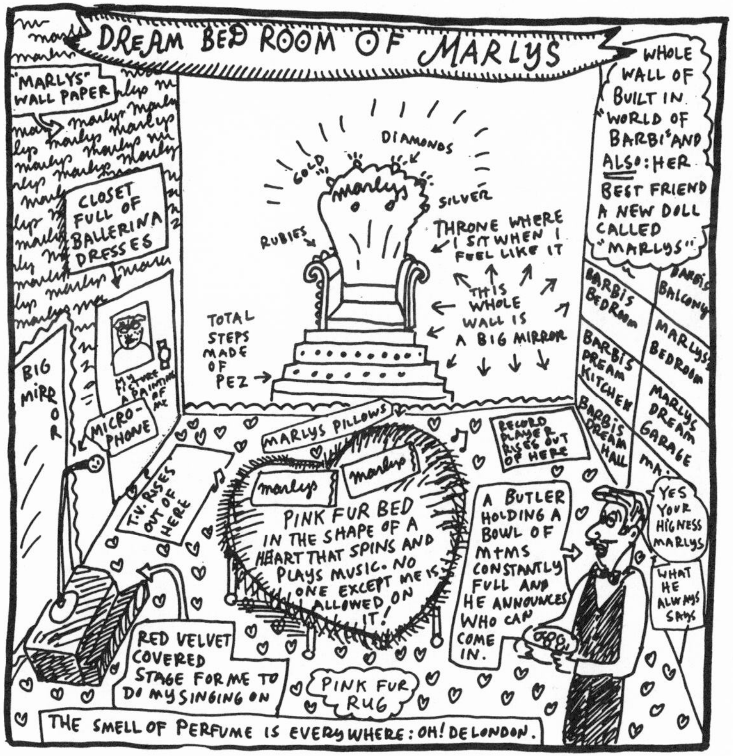
DREAM BED ROOM OF MARLYS
"MARLYS" WALL PAPER
WHOLE WALL OF BUILT IN "WORLD OF BARBI" AND ALSO: HER BEST FRIEND A NEW DOLL CALLED "MARLYS"
DIAMONDS
GOLD
SILVER
marlys
RUBIES
THRONE WHERE I SIT WHEN I FEEL LIKE IT
CLOSET FULL OF BALLERINA DRESSES
THIS WHOLE WALL IS A BIG MIRROR
TOTAL STEPS MADE OF PEZ
BARBIS BEDROOM
BARBIS BALCONY
BARBIS DREAM KITCHEN
MARLYS BEDROOM
BARBIS DREAM HALL
MARLYS DREAM GARAGE
BIG MIRROR
MY PICTURE A PAINTING OF ME
MICRO-PHONE
MARLYS PILLOWS
RECORD PLAYER RISES OUT OF HERE
T.V. RISES OUT OF HERE
marlys
marlys
PINK FUR BED IN THE SHAPE OF A HEART THAT SPINS AND PLAYS MUSIC. NO ONE EXCEPT ME IS ALLOWED ON IT!
A BUTLER HOLDING A BOWL OF M+MS CONSTANTLY FULL AND HE ANNOUNCES WHO CAN COME IN.
YES YOUR HIGNESS MARLYS
WHAT HE ALWAYS SAYS
RED VELVET COVERED STAGE FOR ME TO DO MY SINGING ON
PINK FUR RUG
THE SMELL OF PERFUME IS EVERYWHERE: OH! DE LONDON.

MARLYS' LOVE
BY LYNDA BARRY © 1988
MY COUSIN MARLYS WAS BENDING OVER ONE DAY, LOOKING AT SOME ANTS, WHEN A TEENAGER NAMED RICHARD CAME THROUGH THE GATE WITH A TENNIS RACQUET LOOKING FOR MARLYS' SISTER, MAYBONNE.
WHEN HE WALKED BY MARLYS HE SAID "HI, SQUIRT" AND TAPPED THE TENNIS RACQUET ON HER BEHIND LIKE YOU DO WHEN ANYBODY'S BENT OVER, AND WHEN MARLYS STOOD UP, SHE WAS IN LOVE.

MAYBONNE'S VOICE CAME OUT THE FRONT DOOR SAYING JUST A SEC SO RICHARD SAT DOWN ON THE TOP STEP AND MARLYS STOOD ON THE BOTTOM ONE AND SAID WANT TO SEE ME DO THE MEXICAN HAT DANCE?
IT WAS HER SPECIALTY.

THE UPSTAIRS WINDOW SHOVED OPEN AND MAYBONNE'S HEAD CAME OUT YELLING BUG OFF MARLYS, WILL YOU? BUT NO, SHE COULDN'T. SHE COULDN'T, SHE COULDN'T, SHE JUST COULDN'T.

BIG SISTER
LYNDA BARRY ©1988
MARLYS'S SISTER MAYBONNE HAD THE BIG SLUMBER PARTY OF HER LIFE LAST NIGHT. 12 TEEN-AGE GIRLS ASKING THE OUIJA BOARD DOES DONNY LIKE ME.
YOU PUSHED IT!
DIDN'T EITHER
YOU DID.
AS IF I NEED TO!
E F G
DELORES ALWAYS PUSHES IT!
YES
SHE DOES!
DON'T EITHER! GOD!

FOR FOOD THEY HAD RUFFLES, DORITOS, FRITOS, CHEETOS. FOR POP, YOUR CHOICE OF GRAPE, ORANGE, OR REGULAR. ONE GIRL'S DAD WORKED FOR BEEF JERKY, SO TONS OF THAT. ALSO, MINIATURE MARSHMALLOWS, EVERY COLOR.

WHEN MAYBONNE CAME UPSTAIRS IN HER NEW BABY-DOLL PAJAMA SET TO SNEAK SOME CANDLES FOR THE SEANCE OUT OF THE KITCHEN DRAWER, WE HAD TO ADMIT SHE LOOKED GORGEOUS. SHE WAS SO HAPPY SHE EVEN SAID HI TO US.
WHAT IT IS.

AND SOMETHING HAS HAPPENED TO MARLYS BECAUSE WHEN THE BOYS CAME AROUND THE SIDE OF THE HOUSE IN A LINE TO THE BASEMENT DOOR SHE DIDN'T YELL FOR HER MOM LIKE LAST YEAR. SHE JUST LAID ON HER STOMACH AT THE TOP OF THE STEPS LISTENING TO THEM WHISPERING AND LAUGHING AND BEING SO PERFECT.

DON'T BUG ME
BY LYNDA BARRY ©1988
IT STARTED BY MY COUSIN MAYBONNE SAYING DON'T BUG HER BECAUSE HER BODY WAS GOING THROUGH SPECIAL CHANGES. THEN SHE CALLS UP HER FRIEND SHARON AND WHISPERS "GUESS WHAT, GEORGE IS VISITING."
WHO'S GEORGE?
DON'T BE SO RETARDED.

THEN SHE GOES INTO THE FRONT ROOM AND LAYS DOWN ON HER STOMACH AND LISTENS TO THE SONG "COLOR MY WORLD" OVER AND OVER WHICH MARLYS SAYS MEANS SHE HAS CRAMPS.
MIDOL

AND WHEN MARLYS GOES TO TURN ON THE WONDERFUL WORLD OF DISNEY, MAYBONNE STARTS YELLING NO WAY BECAUSE SHE IS TOO SENSITIVE TO WATCH ANY PROGRAMS OF HELPLESS ANIMALS IN DANGER RIGHT NOW AND MARLYS SAYS THAT'S TOO BAD, TOUGH LUCK, I'M WATCHING IT.

SO THEN MAYBONNE STARTS SCREAMING "MOM! MOM!" AND MARLYS OPENS THE FRONT DOOR AND YELLS OUT "MY NAME IS MAYBONNE AND I CONTROL THE WORLD BECAUSE OF OH! MY UTERUS!" AND I DON'T KNOW WHAT HAPPENED AFTER THAT BECAUSE THE FIRST THING MY AUNT SAID WHEN SHE CAME IN THE ROOM WAS FOR ME TO GO HOME.
227

RING-RING
LYNDA BARRY © 1988
WHEN THE PHONE RANG AND IT WAS THE MAN TELLING MY TEEN AGE COUSIN MAYBONNE SHE GOT THE JOB AT THE DAG'S BEEFY BOY, SHE WAS SO HAPPY SHE SCREAMED.
AUAAGHHH
MY AUNT SCREAMED RIGHT BACK "OVER MY DEAD BODY!" BECAUSE IF YOU DON'T KNOW IT, MAYBONNE IS BOY CRAZY AND DAG'S IS A RACIAL DRIVE-IN OVER BY THE LUMBER YARD. IT'S MIXED.
AND SINCE THEY'VE STOPPED TRYING TO CONTROL THEIR HAIR, ALL HELL HAS BROKEN LOOSE!
MOM
DON'T "MOM" ME YOUNG LADY

SO THEY BOTH START SCREAMING AND SCREAMING UNTIL THEIR VEINS STICK OUT AND MARLYS DECIDES TO COME TO THE RESCUE BY STANDING ON A CHAIR AND SINGING "JESUS LOVES THE LITTLE CHILD-REN" WITH HER ARMS STUCK OUT LIKE SHE'S ON T.V.
AND MY AUNT KEEPS ON YELLING "SOME DAY YOU'LL THANK ME!" AND MAYBONNE KEEPS YELLING "OH NO I WON'T!" AND GUESS WHO WAS RIGHT?

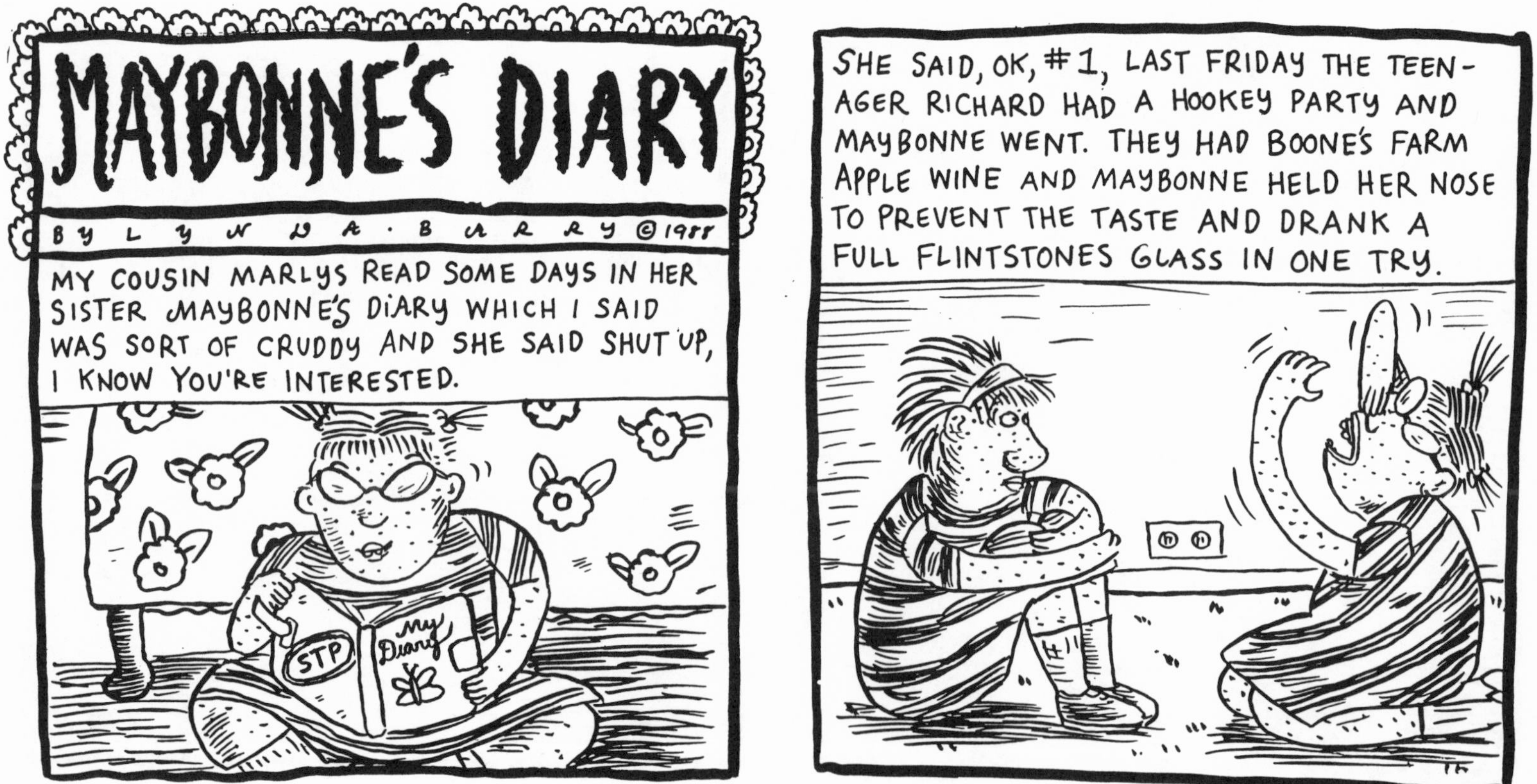
MAYBONNE'S DIARY
BY LYNDA · BARRY ©1988
MY COUSIN MARLYS READ SOME DAYS IN HER SISTER MAYBONNE'S DIARY WHICH I SAID WAS SORT OF CRUDDY AND SHE SAID SHUT UP, I KNOW YOU'RE INTERESTED.
STP
My Diary
SHE SAID, OK, #1, LAST FRIDAY THE TEEN-AGER RICHARD HAD A HOOKEY PARTY AND MAYBONNE WENT. THEY HAD BOONE'S FARM APPLE WINE AND MAYBONNE HELD HER NOSE TO PREVENT THE TASTE AND DRANK A FULL FLINTSTONES GLASS IN ONE TRY.
#1

OK, #2. THEN IT WAS A MAKE OUT PARTY. JOEL GOT SHARON, TONY GOT MARGY AND RICHARD GOT MAYBONNE. THEY FRENCHED 16 TIMES TO THE SONG "LA-LA MEANS I LOVE YOU." IT WAS BEAUTIFUL.

OK #3, RICHARD SAID FOR MAYBONNE TO PUT HER WHOLE HAND ON HIS PANTS BUT MAYBONNE HAD TO BARF AND THEN HER RETAINER WENT IN THE TOILET. NOW SHE DOESN'T KNOW IF RICHARD WAS JUST USING HER OR IF HE'S HER BOYFRIEND.
I SAID TO MARLYS, ARE YOU GOING TO TELL? AND MARLYS SAID TO ME, ARE YOU RETARDED?

WHY, RICHARD, WHY?
BY LYNDA BARRY ©1988
REMEMBER HOW MY COUSIN MAYBONNE COULDN'T TELL IF RICHARD, HER BOYFRIEND, WAS HER BOYFRIEND OR JUST USING HER? WELL, NOW SHE WON'T EAT SO MY AUNT SAYS SHE'S GOING TO HAVE TO WRING HER NECK.
NOW ALL MAYBONNE WANTS TO DO IS STAND IN THE BATHROOM WITH THE RADIO WATCHING HERSELF CRY IN THE MIRROR TO ALL THE SLOW SONGS. AND SHE SCREAMS AT YOU IF YOU SAY YOU HAVE TO GET IN THERE.
I FOUND LOVE ON A TWO WAY STREET AND LOST IT ON A LONELY HIGH WAY

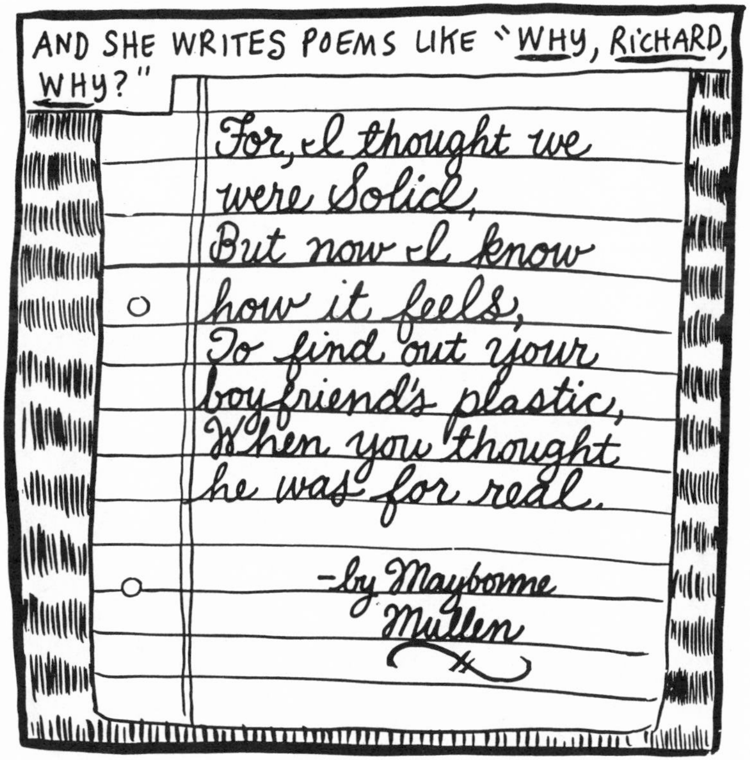
AND SHE WRITES POEMS LIKE "WHY, RICHARD, WHY?"
For, I thought we were Solid,
But now I know how it feels,
To find out your boyfriend's plastic,
When you thought he was for real.
-by Maybonne Mullen

BUT THE WORST IS HOW SHE GOES CRAZY WHEN THE PHONE RINGS BECAUSE SHE WON'T PICK IT UP, SHE JUST STANDS BY IT SCREAMING FOR MARLYS TO HURRY! HURRY! PICK IT UP! PICK IT UP! BUT MARLYS SAYS SHE QUITS BECAUSE EVERY TIME IT'S NOT RICHARD, MAYBONNE TRIES TO HIT HER.
AUGGHH! AUGHHH! MARLYS! MAR-LYS!!
RING
RING
RING
RING

FLY LAND
BY LYNDA SANDSKINK BARRY ©1988
YOU ALREADY KNOW, RIGHT? HOW MY COUSIN FREDDIE IS THE GENIUS OF PROJECTS? THAT'S WHY HE'S ALWAYS FIGHTING MARLYS FOR SHOE BOXES. HE MAKES REALISTIC LANDS IN THEM: THE CAVEMAN VOLCANO TOWN, THE CAVEMAN SEA HUNT, THE CAVEMAN WENT TO VENUS.
RAN WRAP
RED BALL JETS

WHO STARS AS THE CAVEMAN ARE FLIES, THE WORLD'S HARDEST INSECT TO CATCH. JUST FORGET ABOUT TRYING TO CATCH A FLY OUTSIDE. IF THEY COME IN THE HOUSE, OK, YOU CAN TRAP THEM GOOD IN THE CURTAINS AND THAT'S WHY FREDDIE HAS TO ALWAYS LEAVE THE SCREEN DOORS OPEN WHICH HIS MOTHER SAYS HE DOES JUST TO TORMENT HER.
PSST.....
FREDDIE! FLY! FLY!

YOU KNOW THAT SHOE TISSUE PAPER? HE TAPES THAT ON THE TOP AND THEN GO HOLD IT BY THE LAMP FOR LIGHT AND STARE THROUGH THE SARAN WRAP PEEP HOLE AT THE CAVEMAN WALKING AROUND UPSIDE-DOWN EVERYWHERE. SOMETIMES YOU'LL LOOK IN AND NOTICE IT'S TIME FOR A NEW CAVEMAN.
UH-OH... FREDDIE...
THE FLY IN THE VENUS ONE IS DEAD AGAIN.
DID YOU KNOW THAT FLIES WIN FOR INSECT COVERED WITH MOST DEADLY GERMS? WHEN FREDDIE'S MOM CAUGHT HIM HOLDING ONE IN HIS BARE HAND TO GET IT THROUGH THE DOOR OF THE CAVEMAN'S MINIATURE CHRISTMAS, THAT'S WHEN HE HAD TO SWITCH TO SPIDERS WHICH MAY BE CLEANER BUT THEY ARE JUST NOT AS GOOD.
HE MOVE YET?
NOPE. HE'S STILL JUST SITTING THERE BY THE FIRE PLACE.
MAN, SPIDERS ARE TOO LAZY FOR ME
SAME HERE.

MY BEAUTIFUL DRESS
BY LYNDA BARRY ©1988
IT CAME FROM MY COUSIN DEBBIE'S IN THE MAIL. HER MOM WROTE A LETTER THAT DEBBIE COULDN'T FIT IT NOW BECAUSE SHE WAS SO MATURE UPSTAIRS. I ABOUT HAD AN ATTACK WHEN I SAW IT, IT WAS SO BEAUTIFUL.
"PROBABLY DIDN'T EVEN WEAR IT TEN TIMES" MY MOTHER SAID. "THE WAY MY SISTER THROWS MONEY AWAY ON THOSE KIDS, I'M TELLING YOU. MY GOD, THE IRONING THAT HAS TO GO INTO IT! THE SKIRT MUST HAVE TEN YARDS OF FABRIC. TRY IT ON." SHE SAID.